70001617883 5

MACMILLAN READERS

UPPER LEVEL

Founding Editor: John Milne

The Macmillan Readers provide a choice of enjoyable reading materials for learners of English. The series is published at six levels – Starter, Beginner, Elementary, Pre-intermediate, Intermediate and Upper.

Level Control

Information, structure and vocabulary are controlled to suit the students' ability at each level.

The number of words at each level:

Starter	about 300 basic words
Beginner	about 600 basic words
Elementary	about 1100 basic words
Pre-intermediate	about 1400 basic words
Intermediate	about 1600 basic words
Upper	about 2200 basic words

Vocabulary

Some difficult words and phrases in this book are important for understanding the story. Some of these words are explained in the story, some are shown in the pictures, and others are marked with a number like this: …[3]. Phrases are marked with [P]. Words with a number are explained in the *Glossary* at the end of the book and phrases are explained on the *Useful Phrases* page.

Answer Keys

Answer Keys for the *Points for Understanding* and *Exercises* sections can be found at www.macmillanenglish.com/readers.

Audio Download

There is an audio download available to buy for this title. Visit www.macmillanenglish.com/readers for more information.

Contents

A Note About The Author

Oscar Fingal O'Flahertie Wills Wilde was born on October 16th 1854 in Dublin, the capital city of Ireland. Wilde's father, Sir William Wilde, was a famous surgeon. His mother, Jane, was a woman with literary interests. She was well known as the hostess of a literary salon[1] and she was also a writer herself. Using the pen name 'Speranza', she published Irish legends and folk stories. She was also interested in Irish politics. At that time, Ireland was part of the United Kingdom and Speranza was devoted to the cause of freeing her country from British rule. Oscar Wilde was always very close to his extraordinary mother.

Wilde was educated at the Portora Royal School at Enniskillen, then at Trinity College, Dublin, and finally at Magdalen College, Oxford. At Oxford, Wilde studied Greek, Latin and ancient history. He was a brilliant student and he achieved a first class degree. Besides this, he also won the Newdigate Prize for poetry. Wilde also became very interested in aesthetics[2] at Oxford and was influenced[3] by the works of two famous authors who wrote about the theory of beauty – John Ruskin and Walter Pater.

Wilde's earlier career as a writer centred mostly on poems and short stories. Some of the stories were written for his two sons – he had married Constance Lloyd in 1884 and soon after the couple had had Cyril and Vyvyan. Many of the stories are still read and admired – *The Happy Prince*, *Lord Arthur Savile's Crime*, *The Canterville Ghost*, *The Portrait of* Mr *W. H.*, for example. Wilde became famous – even infamous[4] – with the publication of his only novel, *The Picture of Dorian Gray*, a classic of 'decadent'[5] literature, in 1890.

During this period, Wilde was also trying to influence people's taste in clothes, the decoration of their houses and the kind of furniture they bought. He toured Britain and the United States lecturing on these subjects, as well as on literary topics. He was not always taken seriously – in fact he was often satirized[6] in the press, in novels and even on the stage.

Wilde's main interest in the early 1890s was the writing of plays. He wrote several serious plays, including *Salomé* (which he wrote in French) and *A Florentine Tragedy*, and four comedies, *Lady Windermere's Fan*, *A Woman of No Importance*, *An Ideal Husband* and *The Importance of Being Earnest*, all of them full of wit and epigrams[7].

Soon after the first performance of *The Importance of Being Earnest* in 1895, Wilde's wife divorced him and in his later years, he went to live in France. He died there from meningitis on November 30th 1900. Two works from this later period of his life were published – *De Profundis* (a collection of letters) and a poem, *The Ballad of Reading Gaol*, which is centred on the thought that each man kills the thing he loves.

Oscar Wilde is now remembered for his novel, his light-hearted stories and his comedies. His more serious works have almost been forgotten. But we should remember that several of them were made into musical works in the early twentieth century – Richard Strauss's opera *Salomé* is based on Wilde's play of that name and Alexander von Zemlinsky wrote an operatic version of *A Florentine Tragedy* and another opera, *Der Zwerg*, based on Wilde's short story *The Birthday of the Infanta*. Franz Schreker and John Alden Carpenter both wrote music for ballets based on that story too.

Wilde's most popular works have also interested film-makers: *The Picture of Dorian Gray* was filmed in 1945 and again in 2009. There have been two major films of *The Importance of Being Earnest*, one made in 1952 and the other in 2002.

A Note About This Play

Wilde gave *The Importance of Being Earnest* – his last and, many believe, best play – a subtitle: *A Trivial*[8] *Comedy for Serious People*. And he wrote that the play 'has its philosophy: that we should treat all the trivial things in life seriously, and all the serious things of life with sincere triviality'. The serious matter treated with the most triviality in the play is marriage. Like many comedies, *The Importance of Being Earnest* ends with impending[9] marriages, but by then Wilde has used the play to attack and satirize marriage as it was understood by the upper classes of Victorian[10] England.

The play certainly takes some ideas from several other late-Victorian comedies: W. S. Gilbert's *Engaged* and Lestocq and Robson's *The Foundling* are often mentioned as important sources. But most English comedies of that period are written in a tradition that began with the ancient Roman comedies of Plautus and Terentius.

Wilde wrote the play in the late summer and autumn of 1894. His first version of the play was in four acts, like his other comedies, but the final text was reduced to three acts. In making the changes, Wilde was helped by George Alexander, who directed and acted in the first production, which opened on February 14th 1895 in London. Together they removed a sub-plot[11] and concentrated the action entirely on the double marriage plot, which resulted in a play of great technical perfection. The first-night audience must have enjoyed watching this very subversive[12] account of love and marriage on Saint Valentine's Day – the day of love.

Wilde's humorous attack on the social habits of the Victorian upper classes uses satire and the constant inversion[13] of accepted ideas of normal behaviour and attitudes as its weapons. The play is full of jokes, but it is very important to remember that they are mostly jokes between the author and the audience – the characters on the stage don't hear them as jokes; they don't laugh. The title of the play itself turns out to be a joke. Earnest is a 'pun' – or a play on words – based on the fact that the adjective 'earnest', meaning 'serious and sincere', has the same pronunciation as the man's name 'Ernest'. Both the young women in the play come to think they are engaged to young men called Ernest, when in fact neither of the men really has that name. Both men sometimes use the name to take advantage of social situations in ways that show their basic *un*seriousness and lack of earnestness.

Wilde attacks many things about upper class society in *The Importance of Being Earnest*. The play's main satirist and inverter of society's beliefs and opinions, Algernon, even pretends to have a reversed view of class relations. What use are the lower classes, he asks us, if they do not set a good example to the upper classes? Both the lead male characters are cynical[14] and decadent young men. They – especially Algernon – are like comic equals to Dorian Gray, the wicked hero of Wilde's horror novel. But while Dorian Gray is guilty of great wickedness, the worst sin that Algernon demonstrates is a kind of mild greed – he loves sandwiches and cakes. And Jack's deviousness[15] is intended for nothing worse than escaping boredom.

Despite Algernon's cynicism about marriage in general – he alters[16] the well-known proverb 'marriages are made in Heaven' to 'divorces are made in Heaven' – he, like his friend Jack, becomes enthusiastic about marriage when it affects *him*. They both exhibit at least *some* conventional attitudes about proposing to their intended brides. Social conventions say that the men should make the first move, while the young women should appear shy and meek[17]. However, the young women in the play prove to be so 'modern' and cynical in their own approaches to the traditions of proposal and engagement that they leave the men far behind. They are so impatient with the conventions that they have accepted the men's proposals before they have been made – in Cecily's case before she has even met her fiancé[18] – simply because they are both called Ernest.

The young women's 'modernity' is even more clearly demonstrated when Wilde makes fun of the serious ideas of repentance[19] and forgiveness, which were important to Victorian society. Having found out that they have been deceived[20] over their fiancés' names, Gwendolen and Cecily watch Algernon and Jack for signs of repentance. They are so eager to forgive, however, that they will accept almost anything as such a sign. 'They have been eating muffins[21]. That looks like repentance to me,' says Cecily. This line sums up[22] the attitude of the main female characters perfectly.

The other main character in the play, Lady Bracknell, is more complicated. In some ways, Wilde portrays her as a 'dinosaur' with very fixed, old-fashioned beliefs about good families and education. Jack cannot marry her daughter because his parents are unknown, she says. Indeed her anger at the circumstances of Jack's discovery in a handbag as a baby is the play's most famous moment. And when Jack claims that Algernon is devious, Lady Bracknell claims that this is impossible because he was educated at Oxford University.

But in other ways, Wilde shows Lady Bracknell to be a realist. She accepts the inversion of the old stereotypes whereby poor women married rich men for their money, and she sees nothing wrong in the idea of her poor but aristocratic[23] nephew, Algernon, marrying the very rich Cecily for *her* money. By the late nineteenth century, this kind of marriage was a reality in Britain, even if people sometimes pretended differently.

When Lady Bracknell tells her daughter that she is certainly *not* Jack's fiancée, and that she (Lady Bracknell) or her husband will tell Gwendolen when she is engaged, Wilde is not joking about arranged marriages. This would not have been a joke to his audience.

In fact, the main idea of the London 'season'[24] at that time was that it provided a series of parties and dances at which parents of eighteen-year-old girls from 'good' families (or 'good society') could introduce them to 'eligible'[25] young men. The idea was that by the end of the season, all the girls would be engaged to someone from an equally 'good' family. Lady Bracknell explains that Jack is not on her list of eligible men, which she shares with other aristocratic ladies. Here, Wilde is making fun of the way such ladies treat marriage as a kind of market-trading.

A final thing to mention is the upper class custom of 'afternoon tea'. Afternoon tea is served in both Acts One and Two of the play. This was not just a drink, but a light meal served late in the afternoon. It consisted of thin sandwiches (usually containing cucumber) as well as bread and butter, cakes of various kinds and tea to drink.

Wilde made his portrayal of a section of the society of his time cynical and humorous, but it was very recognizable. So *The Importance of Being Earnest* was a great success when it opened in London in 1895. It was successfully brought back to the stage not long after Wilde's death and has been a popular favourite in the British theatre ever since.

The People In This Play

Jack Worthing, also known as Ernest Worthing; a rich bachelor[26]

Algernon Moncrieff, Jack's friend; also a rich bachelor. He is a little younger than Jack. His friends call him Algy.

Lady Augusta Bracknell, Algernon's aunt

Gwendolen Fairfax, Lady Bracknell's daughter

Cecily Cardew, Jack Worthing's ward[27]

Miss Laetitia Prism, a middle-aged spinster; Cecily's governess[28]

Canon[29] **Frederick Chasuble**, an elderly clergyman

Lane, Algernon's servant

Merriman, Jack's servant

Act One

[The living room of Algernon Moncrieff's flat in Mayfair, London. Lane is arranging afternoon tea on a table. Algernon enters]

Algernon: Lane, have you made the cucumber sandwiches for Lady Bracknell's tea?

Lane: Yes, sir. *[Handing them to Algernon on a silver tray]*

Algernon: *[Looking carefully at them, taking two and sitting down on the sofa]* Oh, by the way[P], Lane, I looked at your notebook. I noticed that when Lord Shoreman and Mr Worthing dined with me on Thursday night, eight bottles of champagne were drunk.

Lane: Yes, sir; eight bottles.

Algernon: Why is it that, in a bachelor's home, the servants always drink the champagne? I just ask because I am interested, Lane.

Lane: I think that it is because the champagne is better in a bachelor's home. I have noticed that the champagne in married people's homes is rarely very good.

Algernon: Good heavens[P]! Is marriage so depressing?

Lane: I believe marriage is very pleasant, sir. I haven't had much experience of it myself. I have only been married once, and that was because of a misunderstanding[30] between myself and a young person.

Algernon: *[Lazily, without interest]* I am not very interested in your family life, Lane.

Lane: No, sir; it is not a very interesting subject. I never think of it myself.

Algernon: That is very understandable. Well, thank you, Lane.

[Lane goes off]

Algernon: *[To himself]* Lane's views on marriage seem very casual. Really, if the servants don't set us a good example, what on earth is the use of them? They seem to have no morals[31].

[Lane enters]

Lane: Mr Ernest Worthing is here, sir.

[Jack enters. Lane goes off]

Algernon: How are you, my dear Ernest? What brings you to town?

Jack: Oh, pleasure brings me, pleasure, of course! What else should bring one anywhere? You're eating as usual, I see, Algy!

Algernon: *[Very formally]* I believe it is normal in good society to have some light refreshment at five o'clock. *[In a normal voice]* Where have you been since last Thursday?

Jack: *[Sitting down on the sofa]* In the country.

Algernon: What on earth do you do in the country?

Jack: *[Taking off his gloves]* When one is in town one entertains oneself. When one is in the country one entertains other people. It is very boring.

Algernon: And who are the people you entertain?

Jack: Oh, neighbours, neighbours!

Algernon: Have you got nice neighbours in your part of Shropshire[32]?

Jack: No, they're all horrid. I never speak to any of them.

Algernon: You must entertain them very much, then! *[Going over to the table and taking a sandwich]* By the way, Shropshire *is* where you come from, is it not?

Jack: Shropshire? Yes, of course. My dear fellow[33]! Why are all these cups here? Why cucumber sandwiches? Why are you being so extravagant[34]? Who is coming to tea?

Algernon: Oh, just Aunt Augusta and Gwendolen.

Jack: How perfectly delightful!

Algernon: Yes, but I am afraid Aunt Augusta won't be happy that you're here.

Jack: And why is that?

Algernon: My dear fellow, the way that you flirt[35] with Gwendolen is perfectly disgraceful. It is almost as bad as the way Gwendolen flirts with you.

Jack: I am in love with Gwendolen. I have come to town in order to propose marriage to her.

Algernon: I thought you had come to town for pleasure. I call a marriage proposal business.
Jack: How very unromantic you are!
Algernon: I really don't think proposing is romantic. It is *very* romantic to be in love. But there is nothing romantic about a proposal. Someone might accept. They usually do, I believe. Then the exciting time is over. The most important thing about romance is the uncertainty. If I ever marry, I'll certainly try to forget that I am married.
Jack: I believe you, dear Algy. The Divorce Court was especially invented for people with memories like yours.
[Jack puts out his hand to take a cucumber sandwich; Algernon immediately stops him]
Algernon: Oh, there is no point in thinking about that. Divorces are made in Heaven. Please don't touch the cucumber sandwiches. They were ordered specially for Aunt Augusta. *[Taking a sandwich himself and eating it]*
Jack: Well, you have been eating them all the time.
Algernon: That is different. She is my aunt. *[Offering Jack a different plate]* Have some bread and butter. The bread and butter is for Gwendolen. Gwendolen loves bread and butter.
Jack: *[Helping himself to bread and butter]* And very good bread and butter it is too.
Algernon: Well, my dear fellow, you don't need to eat it all. You are behaving as if you are married to her already. But you are *not* married to her and I don't think you ever will be.
Jack: Why on earth do you say that?
Algernon: Well, firstly, girls never marry the men they flirt with. They don't think it's the right thing to do.
Jack: Oh, that is nonsense!
Algernon: It isn't. It's true. *[Taking two more sandwiches]* That's why one sees such a large number of bachelors all over the place. And secondly, I don't give my consent[36].
Jack: Your consent!

Please don't touch the cucumber sandwiches. They were ordered specially for Aunt Augusta.

Algernon: Gwendolen is my cousin. And before I allow you to marry her, you will have to clear up[37] the matter of Cecily.
[Algernon rings a bell]
Jack: Cecily? What on earth do you mean, Algy? I don't know anyone called Cecily.
[Lane enters]
Algernon: Lane, bring me the cigarette case which Mr Worthing left last time he dined here.
Lane: Yes, sir.
[Lane goes off. Algernon takes the last of the cucumber sandwiches]
Jack: Have you had my cigarette case all this time? I wish you had told me. I have been writing letters to the police about it. I nearly offered a large reward.
Algernon: Well, I wish you *would* offer a large reward. I am very poor at the moment.
Jack: There is no point in offering a large reward now that you've found it.
[Lane enters with the cigarette case on a silver tray. Algernon takes it immediately. Lane goes off]
Algernon: I think that is mean of you, Ernest, I must say[P]. *[Opening the case and examining it]* However, it doesn't matter. Now I look at the inscription[38] inside, I see that this isn't yours.
Jack: Of course it's mine. *[Moving towards Algernon]* You have seen me with it a hundred times, and you shouldn't be reading what is written inside it. It is very impolite to read a private cigarette case.
Algernon: Oh! It is ridiculous to have rules about what one should read and what one shouldn't. Most of modern culture depends on reading what one shouldn't read.
Jack: I know that, and I am not going to discuss modern culture. I simply want my cigarette case back.
Algernon: Yes; but this isn't your cigarette case. This cigarette case is a present from someone called Cecily. And you said you don't know anyone called Cecily.

Jack: Well, if you want to know, Cecily is my aunt.
Algernon: Your aunt?
Jack: Yes. She is a charming old lady. Just give it back to me, Algy.
Algernon: *[Going behind the sofa]* But why does she call herself 'little Cecily' if she is your aunt? *[Reading]* 'From little Cecily, with all her love.'
Jack: *[Going to the front of the sofa and kneeling on it]* My dear fellow, some aunts are tall. Some aunts are not tall. My aunt should be allowed to decide her height for herself. You seem to think that every aunt should be like your aunt, Lady Bracknell! That is ridiculous. Now, give me back my cigarette case. *[Following Algernon all around the room]*
Algernon: Yes. But why does your aunt call you her uncle? *[Reading]* 'From little Cecily, with all her love to her dear Uncle Jack.' I don't object to an aunt being a small aunt. But why does an aunt, whatever her size, call her own nephew 'uncle'? I don't understand. And your name isn't Jack; it is Ernest.
Jack: It isn't Ernest; it's Jack.
Algernon: You have always told me that your name is Ernest. I have introduced you to everyone as Ernest. You answer to the name Ernest. You look as if your name is Ernest. You are the most earnest-looking person I have ever seen in my life. It is perfectly ridiculous to tell me your name isn't Ernest. It is on your visiting cards[39]. Here is one of them. *[Taking it from a case]* 'Mr Ernest Worthing, B.4, The Albany, London.' I'll keep this as proof that your name is Ernest. Don't ever try to deny it to me or to Gwendolen or to anyone else. *[Putting the card in his pocket]*
Jack: Well, my name is Ernest in town and Jack in the country, and the cigarette case was given to me in the country.
Algernon: That does not explain why your small Aunt Cecily calls you her dear uncle. My dear fellow, you had better tell me everything. Go on! I have always suspected that you were a secret Bunburyist and now I am quite[40] sure.

Jack: Bunburyist? What on earth do you mean by a Bunburyist?
Algernon: I'll tell you the meaning of Bunburyist when you tell me why you are Ernest in town and Jack in the country.
Jack: Well, give me my cigarette case first.
Algernon: Here it is. *[Handing Jack the cigarette case]* Now give me your explanation and please make it unbelievable. *[Sitting on the sofa]*
Jack: My dear fellow, there is nothing unbelievable about my explanation. In fact, it's perfectly ordinary. I was brought up by an old gentleman called Thomas Cardew. He adopted me when I was a little boy and he made me the guardian of his granddaughter, Miss Cecily Cardew, in his will[41]. Cecily is my ward and calls me uncle because she respects me, although you wouldn't understand that! You don't understand respect. Cecily lives in my house in the country and is looked after by her excellent governess, Miss Prism.
Algernon: Where is your house in the country, by the way?
Jack: That is nothing to do with you, my dear fellow. I am not going to invite you there ... but I will tell you honestly that the house is not in Shropshire.
Algernon: I guessed that, my dear fellow! I have Bunburyed all over Shropshire twice. Now, go on. Why are you Ernest in town and Jack in the country?
Jack: My dear Algy, I don't know whether you will understand. You are not a very serious person. I will try to explain it to you. I am a responsible guardian and I have to behave well all the time in the country. It is my duty. But it is not very good for my health or my happiness. So, when I want to leave the country and come to town, I pretend to have a younger brother called Ernest. I tell everyone that he lives in The Albany and that he gets into the most terrible trouble. That, my dear Algy, is the truth.
Algernon: You *are* a Bunburyist! I was right to say you were a Bunburyist. You are one of the most advanced Bunburyists I know.

Jack: What on earth do you mean?
Algernon: You have invented a younger brother called Ernest so that you can come to town as often as you like. I have invented an invalid[42] called Bunbury so that I can go to the country as often as I like. When I pretend to visit him, I call it Bunburying. And I call someone who visits imaginary people a Bunburyist. Bunbury is very valuable. For example, if it wasn't for Bunbury's very bad health, I wouldn't be able to dine with you tonight. I should be dining with Aunt Augusta.
Jack: I haven't asked you to dine with me tonight.
Algernon: I know. You are very careless about sending out invitations. It is very foolish of you. Nothing annoys people more than not receiving invitations.
Jack: You ought to dine with your Aunt Augusta.
Algernon: I don't have any intention of dining with Aunt Augusta. Firstly, I dined there on Monday and once a week is enough time to spend with one's relations. Secondly, Aunt Augusta will either give me two women to talk to at dinner or none. And thirdly, I know that tonight she will make me sit next to Mary Farquhar, who always flirts with her own husband across the dinner table. It is not very pleasant. In fact, respectable women should not behave like that … and more and more women are doing it. The number of women in London who flirt with their own husbands is terrible. It looks so bad. Well, now I know that you are a Bunburyist, I want to talk to you about Bunburying. I want to tell you the rules.
Jack: I am *not* a Bunburyist. If Gwendolen agrees to marry me, I am going to kill my brother. In fact, I think I will kill him anyway. Cecily is a little too interested in him. So I am going to get rid of Ernest. And I think you should kill Mr … your invalid friend with the ridiculous name.
Algernon: Nothing will make me kill Bunbury, and, if you ever get married, you will be glad to know Bunbury. A man who marries without knowing Bunbury will have a very boring marriage.

Jack: That is nonsense. If I marry a charming girl like Gwendolen, I certainly won't want to know Bunbury.
Algernon: Then your wife will want to know him. You don't understand that in married life three is company and two is none.
Jack: Don't try to be cynical. It's perfectly easy to be cynical.
Algernon: My dear fellow, it isn't easy to be anything these days. There is so much competition. *[There is the sound of a doorbell being rung for a long time]* Ah! That must be Aunt Augusta. Only relatives ring like that. Now, I will take her out of the room for ten minutes so that you can propose to Gwendolen. So I can dine with you tonight, can't I?
Jack: I suppose so, if you want to.
Algernon: Good.
[Lane enters]
Lane: Lady Bracknell and Miss Fairfax are here, sir.
[Algernon goes forward to meet them. Lady Bracknell and Gwendolen enter]
Lady Bracknell: Good afternoon, dear Algernon. I hope you are behaving very well.
Algernon: I'm feeling very well, Aunt Augusta.
Lady Bracknell: Feeling very well is not the same as behaving very well. In fact, the two things rarely go together.
Algernon: *[To Gwendolen]* Good heavens, you are smart!
Gwendolen: I am always smart! Aren't I, Mr Worthing?
Jack: You're quite perfect, Miss Fairfax.
Gwendolen: Oh! I hope I am not perfect. There would be no room for development and I intend to develop in every direction.
[Gwendolen and Jack sit down together in a corner of the room]
Lady Bracknell: I am sorry if we are a little late, Algernon, but I had to visit Lady Harbury. I hadn't seen her since her poor husband died. She has changed very much; she looks quite twenty years younger. And now I'll have a cup of tea and one of those nice cucumber sandwiches you promised me.
Algernon: Certainly, Aunt Augusta. *[Going over to the tea table]*

Lady Bracknell: Will you come and sit here, Gwendolen?
Gwendolen: Thanks, Mama, I'm quite comfortable over here.
Algernon: *[Picking up the empty plate of sandwiches in horror]* Good heavens! Lane! Why are there no cucumber sandwiches? I ordered them specially.
Lane: *[Seriously]* There were no cucumbers in the market this morning, sir. I went there twice.
Algernon: No cucumbers?
Lane: No, sir.
Algernon: Thank you, Lane. You may go.
Lane: Thank you, sir. *[Goes off]*
Algernon: I am very upset that there were no cucumbers, Aunt Augusta.
Lady Bracknell: It doesn't matter, Algernon. I had some crumpets with Lady Harbury.
Algernon: I hear that her hair has turned quite blonde from grief.
Lady Bracknell: It certainly has changed its colour. I do not know why, of course. *[Algernon takes her a cup of tea]* Thank you. I've got quite a treat for you at dinner tonight, Algernon. I am going to seat you next to Mary Farquhar. She is such a nice woman and she is so sweet to her husband. It's delightful to watch them.
Algernon: I am afraid, Aunt Augusta, I cannot dine with you tonight after all.
Lady Bracknell: *[Frowning[43]]* I hope you can, Algernon. There will be thirteen people at the dining table if you aren't there. That is unlucky. Your uncle will have to eat upstairs. Fortunately, he often has to do that.
Algernon: It is terribly disappointing to me, but I've had a telegram[44] to say that my poor friend Bunbury is very ill again. *[Smiling quickly at Jack]* They think I should be with him.
Lady Bracknell: It is very strange. Mr Bunbury seems to suffer from very bad health.
Algernon: Yes, indeed. He is a permanent invalid.
Lady Bracknell: Well, Algernon, I think it's about time[p] that

It is very strange. Mr Bunbury seems to suffer from very bad health.

Mr Bunbury decides whether he is going to live or die. I don't sympathize with invalids. Illness should not be encouraged in others. One should be healthy. Could you ask Mr Bunbury not to be ill on Saturday? I am holding a reception[45] and I want you to organize the music. People talk during performances of music and I want to encourage them to talk, particularly since it is the end of the London season and they have nearly run out of things to say.
Algernon: I'll speak to Bunbury, Aunt Augusta, if he is still conscious. I think I can promise you that he will be well by Saturday. Of course, the music is a problem. You see, if one plays *good* music, people don't listen and if one plays *bad* music, people don't talk. But I will show you the programme of music I have chosen if you will come into the music room for a moment.
Lady Bracknell: Thank you, Algernon. It is very thoughtful of you.
[Lady Bracknell and Algernon go into the music room, Gwendolen remains behind]
Jack: It's been a charming day, Miss Fairfax.
Gwendolen: Please don't talk about the weather, Mr Worthing. When people talk to me about the weather, I always feel quite certain they mean something else and I get nervous.
Jack: I do mean something else.
Gwendolen: I thought so. In fact, I am never wrong.
Jack: I would like to talk to you about the 'something else' while Lady Bracknell is out of the room.
Gwendolen: Then talk about it quickly. Mama often comes back into a room suddenly.
Jack: *[Nervously]* Miss Fairfax, ever since I met you, I have admired you more than any girl … I have met ever since … I met you.
Gwendolen: Yes, I am quite well aware of that. I was always fascinated by you – even before I met you. *[Jack looks at her in amazement]* We live in an age of ideals[46] – any expensive monthly magazine will tell you that – and my ideal has always been to

love someone called Ernest. When Algernon mentioned he had a friend called Ernest, I knew I would love you.
Jack: Do you really love me, Gwendolen?
Gwendolen: Very much!
Jack: Darling! You don't know how happy you have made me.
Gwendolen: My own Ernest!
Jack: But could you love me if my name wasn't Ernest?
Gwendolen: But your name *is* Ernest.
Jack: Yes, I know it is. But what if it was something else? Couldn't you love me then?
Gwendolen: *[Cleverly]* Ah! But you *are* called Ernest, so there is no reason to think about you not being called Ernest.
Jack: Personally, darling, I don't really like the name Ernest ... I don't think the name suits me.
Gwendolen: It suits you perfectly. It is a wonderful name. It is musical.
Jack: Well, really, Gwendolen, I think there are a lot of nicer names. I think that Jack, for instance, is a charming name.
Gwendolen: Jack? ... No, there is very little music in the name Jack. It does not excite me. I have known several Jacks and they all were very ordinary. I feel pity for any woman who is married to a man called Jack. I think the only really good name is Ernest.
Jack: Gwendolen, I must get baptized[47] at once ... I mean we must get married at once. There is no time to lose.
Gwendolen: *[Shocked]* Married, Mr Worthing?
Jack: Well ... you know that I love you and you told me, Miss Fairfax, that you love me.
Gwendolen: I do love you. But you haven't proposed to me yet. Nothing has been said about marriage.
Jack: Well ... may I propose to you now?
Gwendolen: I think that this would be an excellent time to propose to me. And I will tell you now that I will accept you so that you aren't worried.
Jack: Gwendolen!

Gwendolen: Yes, Mr Worthing? What are you going to say to me?
Jack: You know what I am going to say to you.
Gwendolen: Yes, but you haven't said it.
Jack: Gwendolen, will you marry me? *[Going down on his knees]*
Gwendolen: Yes, of course I will. You have taken a long time to ask. I am afraid you have had very little experience of proposing.
Jack: My dear, I have never loved anyone in the world but you.
Gwendolen: Yes, but men often practise proposing. My brother, Gerald, often proposes to people. All my friends tell me. What wonderful blue eyes you have, Ernest! They are quite, quite blue. I hope you will always look at me like that, especially when there are other people in the room.
[Lady Bracknell enters]
Lady Bracknell: Mr Worthing! Get up from that position. It is not respectable to behave like that.
Gwendolen: Mama! *[Jack tries to stand up but Gwendolen makes him stay in a kneeling position]* Please go away. Mr Worthing has not finished yet.
Lady Bracknell: Finished what, may I ask?
Gwendolen: I am engaged to be married to Mr Worthing, Mama. *[Jack stands up]*
Lady Bracknell: Pardon me, you are not engaged to anyone, Gwendolen. When you are engaged to someone, I, or your father, will inform you of the fact. An engagement should come as a surprise to a young girl. A pleasant surprise or an unpleasant surprise. It is not something that she is allowed to arrange for herself. ... And now, I have a few questions to ask you, Mr Worthing. While I am asking these questions, you, Gwendolen, will wait for me in the carriage[48].
Gwendolen: Mama!
Lady Bracknell: Wait in the carriage, Gwendolen! *[Gwendolen goes to the door. She and Jack kiss their hands and pretend to blow the kisses to each other behind Lady Bracknell's back. Lady Bracknell*

looks around for the cause of the noise. Finally she turns round and sees them. Frowning] Gwendolen, I said wait for me in the carriage!

Gwendolen: Yes, Mama. *[Going off, looking back at Jack]*

Lady Bracknell: You can sit down, Mr Worthing. *[Looks in her pocket for a notebook and pencil]*

Jack: Thank you, Lady Bracknell, I prefer to stand.

Lady Bracknell: *[Notebook and pencil in hand]* I must tell you that you are not on my list of eligible young men, although I have the same list as the Duchess of Bolton. We work together during the season. However, I am quite ready to add your name to the list if your answers are satisfactory. Do you smoke?

Jack: Well, yes, I do smoke.

Lady Bracknell: I am glad to hear it. A man should always have an occupation[49]. There are far too many men in London who don't have an occupation. How old are you?

Jack: Twenty-nine.

Lady Bracknell: That's a very good age to get married. I have always believed that a man who wants to get married should know everything or nothing. Which do you know?

Jack: *[After hesitating]* I know nothing, Lady Bracknell.

Lady Bracknell: I am pleased to hear it. I approve of ignorance. I don't approve of modern education. Fortunately, in England at least, education has no effect at all. What is your income?

Jack: It's between seven and eight thousand pounds a year.

Lady Bracknell: *[Making a note in her book]* Do you earn this income from land that you own or from investments[50]?

Jack: From investments.

Lady Bracknell: That is satisfactory. Owning land is neither profitable nor pleasurable – it costs money to look after it when one is alive and then there are taxes when one is dead. That's all I can say about land.

Jack: I have a country house with some land, but I don't depend upon it for my income.

Lady Bracknell: A country house! How many bedrooms? Well, that doesn't matter. I hope you have a house in town. Gwendolen must have a house in town.
Jack: Well, I do have a town house in Belgrave Square but it is rented to Lady Bloxham.
Lady Bracknell: Lady Bloxham? I don't know her.
Jack: Oh, she doesn't go out very much; she's very old.
Lady Bracknell: She's not necessarily respectable even if she is old. What number Belgrave Square?
Jack: 149.
Lady Bracknell: *[Shaking her head disapprovingly]* But that is the unfashionable side of the street. However, that could easily be changed.
Jack: Do you mean the fashion or the side?
Lady Bracknell: *[Very disapprovingly]* Both, if necessary. Now, let us discuss less important details. Are your parents living?
Jack: I have lost both my parents.
Lady Bracknell: To lose one parent, Mr Worthing, is unfortunate; to lose both seems like carelessness. Who was your father? He must have been a wealthy man. Was he a businessman or an aristocrat?
Jack: I am afraid I don't know. Lady Bracknell, I said that I had lost my parents. In fact, my parents lost me … I don't know who I am. I was … well, I was found.
Lady Bracknell: Found?
Jack: The late[51] Mr Thomas Cardew, a very kind and charitable old gentleman, found me and called me 'Worthing' because he had a train ticket for Worthing in his pocket at the time. Worthing is a seaside town.
Lady Bracknell: Where did the kind gentleman who had a train ticket for this seaside town find you?
Jack: *[Seriously]* In a handbag.
Lady Bracknell: A handbag?
Jack: *[Very seriously]* Yes, Lady Bracknell. I was in a handbag – a large, black leather handbag – an ordinary handbag with handles.

Lady Bracknell: Where did Mr Thomas Cardew find this ordinary handbag?
Jack: In the cloakroom[52] at Victoria Station, here in London. It was a mistake. It was given to him instead of his own bag.
Lady Bracknell: In the cloakroom at Victoria Station?
Jack: Yes.
Lady Bracknell: Mr Worthing, I am shocked by what you have just told me. I do not think it is right to be born in a handbag, even if it has handles. And I do not think it is right to be found in a handbag in a cloakroom at a railway station. It is not the way to become a respectable gentleman with a good position in society.
Jack: What is your advice, Lady Bracknell? I would, of course, do anything to make Gwendolen happy.
Lady Bracknell: My advice to you, Mr Worthing, is this – try to find some relations as soon as possible. And try to find at least one parent.
Jack: Well, I don't see how I could possibly do that. I can show you the handbag. It is in a wardrobe at home. I really think that should satisfy you, Lady Bracknell.
Lady Bracknell: Me, sir! It has nothing to do with me! Do you really think that Lord Bracknell would allow our only daughter to marry the son of a cloakroom and form a relationship with a piece of luggage? Goodbye, Mr Worthing!
[Lady Bracknell leaves the room with great dignity[53]]
Jack: Goodbye! *[Algernon starts singing a Wedding March[54] in the music room. Jack looks very angry and goes to the door]* Stop singing that awful tune, Algy!
[The singing stops and Algernon enters cheerfully]
Algernon: Didn't everything work out all right, old fellow? Did Gwendolen refuse to marry you?
Jack: Oh, Gwendolen was fine. She believes we are engaged. Her mother is awful. I've never met such a monster. Oh, I beg your pardon, Algy, I suppose I shouldn't talk about your own aunt in that way in front of you.

Algernon: My dear fellow, I love hearing people being rude about my relations. Relations are simply a boring group of people who don't know how to live and don't know when to die.
Jack: Oh, that is nonsense!
Algernon: It isn't!
Jack: Well, I won't argue about it. You always want to argue about things.
Algernon: Things were made for arguing about.
Jack: If I believed that, I'd shoot myself … *[A pause]* You don't think Gwendolen will become like her mother in a hundred and fifty years, do you, Algy?
Algernon: All women become like their mothers. That is their tragedy. No men become like theirs. That is *their* tragedy.
Jack: Have you said something clever?
Algernon: They were very fine sentences and they are very true.
Jack: I'm tired of cleverness. Everybody is clever nowadays. You meet clever people everywhere. I wish that there were a few fools left in the world.
Algernon: There are.
Jack: I should like to meet them. What do they talk about?
Algernon: The fools? They talk about the clever people, of course.
Jack: What fools!
Algernon: By the way, did you tell Gwendolen the truth about being Ernest in town and Jack in the country?
Jack: My dear fellow, one does not tell the truth to a nice, sweet girl. You have extraordinary ideas about how to behave to a woman!
Algernon: The only way to behave to a woman is to flirt with her if she is pretty. And if she isn't pretty, you must flirt with someone else.
Jack: Oh, that is nonsense.
Algernon: What about your badly behaved brother Ernest? Did you tell her about him?

Jack: Oh, I shall have got rid of him before the end of the week. I'll say he died in Paris of a heart attack. Lots of people die of a heart attack quite suddenly, don't they?
Algernon: Yes, but it's hereditary[55], my dear fellow. It's the sort of thing that runs in families[P]. You had better say that he died of a bad cold.
Jack: Are you sure that a bad cold isn't hereditary?
Algernon: Of course it isn't.
Jack: Very well, then. My poor brother Ernest will die suddenly, in Paris, of a bad cold. That gets rid of him.
Algernon: But you said that your ward ... Miss Cardew ... was a little too interested in your poor brother Ernest. Won't she be very distressed?
Jack: Oh, that's not a problem. Cecily is not a silly romantic girl, I am pleased to say. She eats big meals, goes for long walks and doesn't pay attention to her lessons.
Algernon: I would like to meet Cecily.
Jack: I will make sure that you never meet her. She is extremely pretty and she is just eighteen.
Algernon: Have you told Gwendolen that you have an extremely pretty ward who is just eighteen?
Jack: Oh, one mustn't tell people everything all at once. Cecily and Gwendolen will be great friends, I'm sure. They will be calling each other sister half an hour after they meet.
Algernon: Women only call each other sister after they have called each other lots of other things first. Now, my dear fellow, if we want to get a good table at the restaurant, we must go and change our clothes now. It's nearly seven. I'm hungry.
Jack: *[Irritably]* I never knew a time when you weren't hungry.
Algernon: What shall we do after dinner? Go to a theatre?
Jack: Oh no! One has to listen at the theatre. I hate listening.
Algernon: Well, let us go to the Club[56].
Jack: Oh no! One has to talk at the Club. I hate talking.
Algernon: Well, we could go to the Empire Music Hall[57] at ten.

Jack: The Music Hall? Oh no! I hate looking at things.
Algernon: Well, what shall we do?
Jack: Nothing!
Algernon: Doing nothing is very hard work. However, I don't mind very hard work if there is nothing definite to do.
[Lane enters]
Lane: Miss Fairfax has returned, sir.
[Gwendolen enters. Lane goes off]
Algernon: Gwendolen. Hello!
Gwendolen: Algy, please go away. I have something which I want to say to Mr Worthing in private.
Algernon: Really, Gwendolen. I don't think I can allow you to do that.
Gwendolen: Algy, you are not quite old enough to say things like that. *[Algernon goes to the other side of the room near the fireplace and stands with his back to them]*
Jack: My own darling!
Gwendolen: Ernest, we may never be married. I saw the frown on Mama's face. Few parents these days pay attention to what their children say to them. I was three years old the last time I had any influence over my mother. Ernest, she may stop us from getting married. I may get married to someone else, I may get married again and again – but nothing will ever change my love for you.
Jack: Dear Gwendolen!
Gwendolen: Mama told me the romantic story of your birth. She is displeased about it, but I love it. Your name – Ernest – fascinates me. You are so simple and good-natured and that makes you wonderfully complicated. I've got your town address at The Albany. What is your address in the country?
Jack: The Manor House, Woolton, Hertfordshire.
[Algernon, who has turned round and has been carefully listening, smiles to himself and writes the address on the cuff[58] *of his shirt. Then he picks up a railway timetable from a shelf]*

The Manor House, Woolton, Hertfordshire.

Gwendolen: It may be necessary to do something impetuous[59]. We will have to think carefully about this. I will write to you every day.
Jack: My own one!
Gwendolen: How long will you be in town?
Jack: Till Monday.
Gwendolen: Good! Algy, you may turn round now.
Algernon: Thanks, I have turned round already.
Gwendolen: You may also ring the bell for Lane to take me to the door. *[Algernon rings the bell]*
Jack: Let me take you to the door, my own darling.
Gwendolen: Certainly.
Jack: *[To Lane, who now enters]* I will take Miss Fairfax to the door.
Lane: Yes, sir.
[Jack and Gwendolen go off]
Algernon: Bring me a glass of wine, Lane.
Lane: Yes, sir.
Algernon: Tomorrow, Lane, I'm going Bunburying.
Lane: Yes, sir.
Algernon: I shall probably not be back till Monday. Pack my evening clothes, some casual clothes and all my Bunbury suits ...
Lane: Yes, sir. *[Handing Algernon his glass of wine]*
Algernon: I hope that tomorrow is a fine day, Lane.
Lane: It never is, sir.
Algernon: Lane, you are a pessimist.
Lane: I do my best, sir.
[Jack enters. Lane goes off]
Jack: What a sensible, intelligent girl! The only girl I've ever cared for in my life. *[Algernon is laughing loudly]* What on earth are you laughing at?
Algernon: Oh, I'm a bit worried about poor Bunbury, that is all.
Jack: Your friend Bunbury will get you into trouble one day, you know.

Algernon: I love trouble. It's the only thing which is never serious.
Jack: Oh, that's nonsense, Algy. You never talk anything but nonsense.
Algernon: Nobody ever does.
[Jack shakes his head at him and leaves the room. Algernon lights a cigarette, looks at his shirt-cuff and smiles]

Act Two

[The garden at the Manor House in Woolton, Hertfordshire, Jack Worthing's country home. Miss Prism is sitting at a table. Cecily is watering flowers]

Miss Prism: *[Calling]* Cecily, Cecily! I think that watering flowers is a servant's occupation rather than yours, especially at a moment when the pleasures of education are waiting for you. Your German grammar book is on the table. Please open it at page fifteen. We will do yesterday's lesson again.

Cecily: *[Coming over to the table very slowly]* But I don't like German. It isn't a very pretty language. I know that I look quite ugly after my German lesson.

Miss Prism: Child, your guardian is anxious that you improve yourself in every way. As he was leaving for town yesterday, he reminded me how important your German is. Indeed he always reminds me how important your German is when he is leaving for town.

Cecily: Dear Uncle Jack is so very serious! Sometimes he is so serious that I think he must be ill.

Miss Prism: *[Sitting up very straight in her chair]* Your guardian's health is excellent and his seriousness – indeed his earnestness – is very admirable in such a young man. I do not know anyone else who has such a good sense of duty and responsibility.

Cecily: I suppose that is why he often seems a little bored when we three are together.

Miss Prism: Cecily! I am surprised at you. Mr Worthing has many troubles in his life. You must remember that he is always worried about that unfortunate young man, his brother Ernest.

Cecily: I wish Uncle Jack would allow that unfortunate young man, his brother Ernest, to come here sometimes. We might have a good influence on him, Miss Prism. I am sure that you would. You know German and geology and all kinds of things that influence a man very much. *[Cecily begins to write in her diary]*

Miss Prism: *[Shaking her head]* I do not think that even I could have a good influence on his character. Mr Worthing himself says that his brother's character is weak and indecisive. Indeed, I wouldn't want to have a good influence on him. I do not approve of this modern desire to turn bad people into good people at a moment's notice[P]. I think he should suffer because of his misbehaviour. You must put away your diary, Cecily. I really don't understand why you keep a diary at all.

Cecily: I keep a diary in order to write down the wonderful secrets of my life. If I didn't write them down, I should probably forget all about them.

Miss Prism: Our memory is the diary that we all have with us.

Cecily: Yes, but our memory usually remembers things that have never happened and couldn't possibly have happened. I believe that memory is responsible for all the three-volume novels people write.

Miss Prism: Do not be dismissive[60] of the three-volume novel, Cecily. I wrote one myself a long time ago.

Cecily: Did you really, Miss Prism? How wonderfully clever you are! I hope it did not end happily! I don't like novels that end happily. They depress me so much.

Miss Prism: The good people ended happily. The bad people ended unhappily. That is fiction.

Cecily: I suppose so. But it seems very unfair. And was your novel ever published?

Miss Prism: I am sad to say it was not. The manuscript, unfortunately, was lost. Now, start work, child. There is no point in thinking about these things.

Cecily: *[Smiling]* But I see dear Canon Chasuble coming towards us through the garden.

Miss Prism: *[Standing up and going towards Canon Chasuble]* Canon Chasuble! It is indeed a pleasure to see you.

Chasuble: And how are we today? Miss Prism, you are, I hope, well?

Cecily: Miss Prism has just been complaining of a slight headache. I think that it would do her good to have a short walk with you in the park, Canon Chasuble.
Miss Prism: Cecily, I have not mentioned anything about a headache.
Cecily: No, dear Miss Prism, I know that, but I felt that you had a headache. Indeed, I was thinking about that, and not about my German lesson, when Canon Chasuble arrived.
Chasuble: I hope, Cecily, that you pay attention to your lessons.
Cecily: Oh, I am afraid I do not!
Chasuble: That is strange. If I were Miss Prism's pupil, I would always pay attention. Has Mr Worthing returned from town yet?
Miss Prism: We expect him on Monday afternoon.
Chasuble: Ah, yes, he usually likes to spend his Sundays in London. He is an earnest young man who does not always look for pleasure as, I believe, his younger brother does. I will see you both at church later, shall I?
Miss Prism: I think, dear canon, I will have a walk with you. I find I have a headache after all and a walk might do it good.
Canon Chasuble: It would be a pleasure, Miss Prism, a pleasure. Let us go to the end of the garden and back.
Miss Prism: That would be delightful. Cecily, you will read your *Political Economy* in my absence.
[Miss Prism goes down the garden with Canon Chasuble]
Cecily: Oh horrid *Political Economy*! Horrid German!
[Merriman enters with a visiting card on a silver tray]
Merriman: Mr Ernest Worthing has just arrived from the station. He has brought his luggage with him.
Cecily: *[Taking the card and reading it]* 'Mr Ernest Worthing, B.4, The Albany, London.' He must be Uncle Jack's brother! Have you told him Uncle Jack is in town?
Merriman: Yes, miss. He seemed very disappointed. I told him that you and Miss Prism were in the garden. He said he was anxious to speak to you privately for a moment.

Cecily: Ask Mr Ernest Worthing to come here. And you had better talk to the housekeeper[61] about a bedroom for him.
Merriman: Yes, miss.
[Merriman goes off]
Cecily: *[To herself]* I have never met a really wicked person before. I feel rather frightened. I am so afraid that he will look just like everyone else. *[Algernon enters looking very handsome and fashionable]* Oh dear, he does!
Algernon: *[Raising his hat]* You are my little cousin, Cecily, I'm sure.
Cecily: You are making a strange mistake. I am not little. In fact, I believe I am quite tall for my age. *[Algernon is rather surprised]* But I am your cousin, Cecily. You, I see from your card, are Uncle Jack's brother, my cousin Ernest, my *wicked* cousin Ernest.
Algernon: Oh! I am not really wicked at all, Cousin Cecily. You mustn't think that I am wicked.
Cecily: If you are not wicked, then I think you have been deceiving us all. I hope that you have not been leading a double life. I hope you have not been pretending to be wicked and being really good all the time. That would be hypocrisy[62].
Algernon: *[Looking at her in amazement]* Oh! Of course, I have been rather bad.
Cecily: I'm glad to hear it.
Algernon: In fact, I think that I have been very wicked in my own way.
Cecily: I don't think you should be so proud of that, though I'm sure it must have been very pleasant.
Algernon: It is much pleasanter being here with you.
Cecily: I can't understand why you are here at all. Uncle Jack won't be back from town till Monday afternoon.
Algernon: That is a great disappointment to me. I have to leave for London by the first train on Monday morning. I have a business meeting that I am anxious … to miss!
Cecily: Couldn't you miss it anywhere but in London?

Algernon: No. The appointment is in London.
Cecily: Well, of course, I know that it is important not to attend a business meeting. That is what makes life interesting. But I think you should wait till Uncle Jack arrives. I know he wants to speak to you about your emigration.
Algernon: He wants to speak to me about ... I don't understand!
Cecily: About your emigration. He has gone to town to buy your clothes.
Algernon: I certainly wouldn't let Jack buy my clothes. He has no taste in ties at all.
Cecily: I don't think you will require ties. Uncle Jack is sending you to Australia.
Algernon: Australia! I'd rather die.
Cecily: Well, at dinner on Wednesday he said that you would have to choose between this world, the next world and Australia.
Algernon: Oh well! I don't believe Australia and the next world are very nice. This world is good enough for me, Cousin Cecily.
Cecily: Ah, but are you good enough for it?
Algernon: I'm afraid I'm not. That is why I want you to reform[63] me. Please will you do this, Cousin Cecily.
Cecily: I'm afraid I don't have time this afternoon.
Algernon: Well, would you mind if I reformed myself this afternoon?
Cecily: It is rather ambitious of you. But I think you should try.
Algernon: I will. I feel better already.
Cecily: You are looking a little worse.
Algernon: That is because I am hungry.
Cecily: How thoughtless of me. I should have remembered that someone who is going to reform himself needs regular meals. Please come in.
Algernon: Thank you. May I have a flower for my buttonhole first? I never have any appetite unless I have a flower for my buttonhole. I'd like a pink rose.
Cecily: *[Picking up scissors]* Why? *[Cutting a flower]*

Algernon: Because you are like a pink rose, Cousin Cecily.
Cecily: I don't think that it is right for you to talk to me like that. Miss Prism doesn't say such things to me.
Algernon: Miss Prism must be a very short-sighted old lady. *[Cecily puts the flower in his buttonhole]* You are the prettiest girl I have ever seen.
Cecily: Miss Prism says that good looks are a trap.
Algernon: They are a trap that every sensible man would like to be caught in.
Cecily: Oh, I don't think I would like to catch a sensible man. I wouldn't know what to talk to him about.
[They go into the house. Miss Prism and Canon Chasuble enter]
Miss Prism: You are on your own too much, Canon Chasuble. You should get married.
Chasuble: The Early Church was very much against marriage.
Miss Prism: That is obviously the reason why the Early Church has not lasted to the present day. And you do not seem to realize, dear sir, that a man who remains single becomes a permanent temptation.
Chasuble: But isn't a man equally attractive when he is married?
Miss Prism: No married man is ever attractive except to his wife.
Chasuble: And often, I've been told, he is not even attractive to her.
Miss Prism: That depends on the woman. If she is a mature woman, she can be relied upon. You cannot rely upon a *young* woman. But where is Cecily?
Chasuble: Perhaps she followed us.
[Jack enters from the back of the garden. He is wearing black mourning clothes[64]]
Miss Prism: Mr Worthing!
Chasuble: Mr Worthing!
Miss Prism: This is a surprise. We did not expect you till Monday afternoon.
Jack: *[Shaking Miss Prism's hand in a tragic way]* I have returned

sooner than I expected to. Canon Chasuble, I hope you are well?
Chasuble: Dear Mr Worthing, I hope these black clothes do not mean that something dreadful has happened?
Jack: My brother.
Miss Prism: More shameful debts and bad behaviour?
Chasuble: Is he still leading his wicked life?
Jack: *[Shaking his head]* Dead!
Chasuble: Your brother Ernest is dead?
Jack: Quite dead.
Miss Prism: What a lesson for him! I hope he will learn from this.
Chasuble: Mr Worthing, I offer you my sincere condolences[65]. At least you know that you have always been most generous and forgiving to him.
Jack: Poor Ernest! He had many faults, but it is very, very sad.
Chasuble: Very sad indeed. Were you with him at the end?
Jack: No. He died abroad; in Paris, in fact. I had a telegram last night from the manager of the Grand Hotel in Paris.
Chasuble: Did the telegram mention the cause of death?
Jack: A bad cold, it seems.
Miss Prism: As a man sows, so shall he reap[P].
Chasuble: Charity[66], dear Miss Prism, charity! None of us are perfect. I myself am particularly sensitive to draughts[67]. Will the funeral take place here?
Jack: No. It seems he wanted to be buried in Paris.
Chasuble: In Paris! *[Shaking his head]* I don't think he was being very serious even at the end. You will want me to mention this sad event in church next Sunday. *[Jack presses Canon Chasuble's hand very hard and looks very sad]* My sermon[68] on the mercy of God can be used on any occasion, happy or sad. *[They all sigh]* I have preached it at baptisms, weddings and funerals. The last time I preached it was to the Society for the Prevention of Discontent[69] among the Upper Classes. The Bishop, who was present, liked it very much.

Jack: Ah! That reminds me. You mentioned baptisms, I think, Canon Chasuble? You know how to baptize people, I suppose? *[Canon Chasuble looks very surprised]* I mean you often baptize people, don't you?
Miss Prism: It is, I am sorry to say, one of the canon's most frequent duties. I have often spoken to the poorer classes about it. But they don't take any notice.
Chasuble: But is there any particular child in whom you are interested, Mr Worthing? Your brother was, I believe, unmarried?
Jack: Oh yes.
Miss Prism: *[Bitterly[70]]* People who live just for pleasure are usually unmarried.
Jack: But it is not for any child, dear canon. No! The fact is that I would like to be baptized myself, this afternoon, if you have nothing better to do.
Chasuble: But surely, Mr Worthing, you have been baptized already?
Jack: I don't remember anything about it. Of course, I don't know if you think I am a little too old now.
Chasuble: Not at all. At what time would you like the ceremony performed?
Jack: Oh, I'll come about five o'clock if that would suit you.
Chasuble: Perfectly, perfectly! In fact I have two similar ceremonies to perform at that time – twins who were born in one of the cottages on your estate.
Jack: Oh! I don't think it would be much fun to be baptized along with other babies. It would be childish. Would half-past five be all right?
Chasuble: Of course, of course! *[Taking out his watch from his pocket]* And now, dear Mr Worthing, I will not stay any longer in this house of grief. I ask you not to grieve too much. Bitter trials[P] are often blessings in disguise[P].
Miss Prism: This seems to me to be an extremely obvious blessing. *[Cecily enters from the house]*

Cecily: Uncle Jack! Oh, I am pleased to see you. But what horrible clothes you are wearing. Please go and change them.
Miss Prism: Cecily!
Chasuble: My child! My child!
[Cecily goes towards Jack, who kisses her forehead in a tragic way]
Cecily: What is the matter, Uncle Jack? Please look happy! You look as if you have toothache, and I have got such a surprise for you. Who do you think is in the dining room? Your brother!
Jack: Who?
Cecily: Your brother Ernest. He arrived about half an hour ago.
Jack: What nonsense! I haven't got a brother.
Cecily: Oh, don't say that. He is still your brother even though he has behaved badly in the past. You mustn't be so heartless. I'll tell him to come out. And you will shake hands with him, won't you, Uncle Jack?
[Cecily runs back into the house]
Chasuble: This is very happy news.
Miss Prism: Since we were just getting used to his departure, his sudden return seems very distressing.
Jack: My brother is in the dining room? I don't know what it means. I think it is perfectly ridiculous.
[Algernon and Cecily enter holding hands. They come slowly towards Jack]
Good heavens! *[He waves his hand to try to make Algernon go away]*
Algernon: *[Holding his hand out to Jack]* Brother Jack, I have come from town to tell you that I am very sorry for all the trouble I have given you and that I will behave myself better in future. *[Jack glares[71] at him and doesn't take his hand]*
Cecily: Uncle Jack, are you going to refuse to shake your brother's hand?
Jack: Nothing will make me shake his hand. I think it is disgraceful that he has come here. He knows perfectly well why.
Cecily: Uncle Jack, do be nice. There is some good in everyone.

Good heavens!

Ernest has just been telling me about his poor invalid friend, Mr Bunbury, whom he goes to visit very often. There must be much good in Ernest if he leaves London to sit by the bed of an invalid.

Jack: Oh! He has been talking about Bunbury, has he?

Cecily: Yes, he has told me all about poor Mr Bunbury and his very bad health.

Jack: Bunbury! Well, I don't want him to talk to you about Bunbury or about anything else. It makes me furious.

Algernon: Of course, I agree that I used to behave very badly. But I must say that I think Brother Jack's coldness towards me is very unkind. I expected a better welcome, especially since it is the first time I have come here.

Cecily: Uncle Jack, if you don't shake hands with Ernest, I will never forgive you.

Jack: You will never forgive me?

Cecily: Never, never, never!

Jack: Well, this is the last time I shall ever do it. *[Shaking hands with Algernon and glaring at him]*

Chasuble: It is pleasant to see a perfect reconciliation[72], is it not? I think we should leave the brothers together.

Miss Prism: Cecily, you will come with us.

Cecily: Certainly, Miss Prism. My task of reconciliation is over.

Chasuble: You have done something beautiful today, dear child.

Miss Prism: We must not say these things too soon.

Cecily: I feel very happy.

[They all go off except Jack and Algernon]

Jack: You young scoundrel[73], Algy, you must get out of this place as soon as possible. I don't allow any Bunburying here.

[Merriman enters]

Merriman: I have put Mr Ernest's things in the room next to yours, sir.

Jack: What?

Merriman: Mr Ernest's luggage, sir. I have unpacked it and put it in the room next to your own.

Jack: His luggage?
Merriman: Yes, sir. Three large suitcases, a small suitcase, two hat boxes and a large picnic basket.
Algernon: I'm afraid I can only stay for a week this time.
Jack: Merriman, order the carriage at once. Mr Ernest has suddenly been called back to town.
Merriman: Yes, sir.
[Merriman goes off]
Algernon: What a liar you are, Jack. I have not been called back to town at all.
Jack: Yes, you have.
Algernon: I haven't heard anyone call me.
Jack: Your duty as a gentleman calls you back.
Algernon: My duty as a gentleman has never interfered with my pleasure at all.
Jack: Yes, I quite understand that!
Algernon: Well, Cecily is a darling.
Jack: You are not to talk of Miss Cardew like that. I don't like it.
Algernon: Well, I don't like your clothes. You look perfectly ridiculous in them. Why don't you go upstairs and change? It is perfectly childish to be wearing black clothes for a man who is going to stay in your house for a whole week as a guest.
Jack: You are certainly not staying with me for a whole week. You have got to leave ... by the four o'clock train.
Algernon: I certainly won't leave you while you are in black clothes. That would be very unfriendly.
Jack: Well, will you go if I change my clothes?
Algernon: Yes, if you are not too long. I never saw anybody else who took so long to get dressed, and with such uninteresting results.
Jack: Well, at least that is better than always being overdressed like you.
Algernon: If I am occasionally overdressed, I make up for it by being extremely overeducated.

Jack: Your vanity is silly, your behaviour is outrageous and your presence in my garden is ridiculous. However, you have got to catch the four o'clock train and I hope you will have a pleasant journey back to town. This Bunburying has not been a success for you.

[Jack goes into the house]

Algernon: *[To himself]* I think it has been a *great* success. I'm in love with Cecily and that is wonderful.

[Cecily enters at the back of the garden. She picks up a can and starts watering the flowers]

But I must see her before I go and make arrangements for some more Bunburying. Ah, there she is.

Cecily: Oh, I came back to water the roses. I thought you were with Uncle Jack.

Algernon: He's gone to order the carriage for me.

Cecily: Oh, is he going to take you for a nice drive?

Algernon: He's going to send me away.

Cecily: Then we have to part?

Algernon: I am afraid so. It's a very painful parting.

Cecily: It is always painful to part with new friends. It is easy to bear the absence of old friends, but even a short parting from someone whom one has just met is extremely painful.

Algernon: Thank you.

[Merriman enters]

Merriman: The carriage is at the door, sir.

[Algernon looks sadly at Cecily]

Cecily: It can wait, Merriman … for … five minutes.

Merriman: Yes, miss.

[Merriman goes off]

Algernon: I hope, Cecily, I shall not offend you if I tell you that you seem to me to be perfect in every way.

Cecily: I think that it is very good that you are so honest. If you will allow me, I will copy your words into my diary. *[Going over to a table and starting to write in her diary]*

Algernon: Do you really keep a diary? I'd love to look at it. May I look at it?
Cecily: Oh, no. *[Putting her hand over it]* You see, it is just a young girl's record of her thoughts and impressions, and of course, it is going to be published. When it appears in the form of a book, I hope you will buy a copy. But please don't stop, Ernest. I enjoy writing things down from dictation. I have got to 'perfect in every way'. You can go on. I am quite ready to write down more.
Algernon: *[Rather surprised, coughing]* Ahem! Ahem!
Cecily: Oh, don't cough, Ernest. When one is dictating, one should speak clearly and not cough. Besides, I can't spell a cough. *[Writing as Algernon speaks]*
Algernon: *[Speaking very quickly]* Cecily, ever since I first looked at your wonderful beauty, I have loved you wildly, passionately, devotedly, hopelessly.
Cecily: I don't think that you should tell me you love me wildly, passionately, devotedly, hopelessly. Hopelessly doesn't make much sense, does it?
Algernon: Cecily.
[Merriman enters]
Merriman: The carriage is waiting at the door, sir.
Algernon: Tell it to come to the door next week at the same time.
Merriman: *[Looking at Cecily, who doesn't say anything]* Yes, sir. *[Merriman goes off]*
Cecily: Uncle Jack would be very annoyed if he knew you were staying till next week at the same time.
Algernon: Oh, I don't care about Jack. I don't care about anybody in the whole world except you. I love you, Cecily. You will marry me, won't you?
Cecily: You silly boy! Of course. We have been engaged for the last three months.
Algernon: For the last three months?
Cecily: Yes, it will have been three months on Thursday.

I have got to 'perfect in every way'.

Algernon: But how did we become engaged?
Cecily: Well, ever since Uncle Jack told us he had a very wicked younger brother, you, of course, have been the main topic of conversation between myself and Miss Prism. And a man who is talked about all the time is very attractive. And I fell in love with you, which is probably a bit silly of me.
Algernon: Darling! And when did we become engaged?
Cecily: On the fourteenth of February. I was unhappy that you didn't know I existed, so I made up my mind to decide the matter, one way or the other. After thinking about it for a long time, I decided to accept your proposal of marriage. I decided that we were engaged. And so the next day I bought this little ring for you to give me and I promised you that I would always wear it.
Algernon: Did I give you this? It's very pretty, isn't it?
Cecily: Yes, you've got wonderfully good taste, Ernest. It's the excuse I've given you for leading such a bad life. And this is the box in which I keep all your dear letters. *[Putting a box on the table. Opening the box and bringing out a bundle of letters tied up with a blue ribbon]*
Algernon: *[Sitting beside her]* My letters! But, my own sweet Cecily, I have never written you any letters.
Cecily: You needn't remind me, Ernest. I remember very well that I had to write your letters for you. I always wrote three times a week and sometimes more often.
Algernon: Oh, do let me read them, Cecily.
Cecily: Oh, I couldn't possibly let you do that. They would make you far too conceited[74]. *[Replacing the box]* The three that you wrote me after I had broken off the engagement are so beautiful and so badly spelt that even now they make me cry a little when I read them.
Algernon: But was our engagement ever broken off?
Cecily: Of course it was. On the twenty-second of March. You can see the diary entry if you like. *[Showing her diary]* 'Today I broke off my engagement with Ernest. I feel it is better to do so.

The weather continues to be very pleasant.'

Algernon: But why on earth did you break it off? What had I done? I had done nothing at all. Cecily, I am very hurt indeed to hear that you broke it off. Particularly when the weather was so pleasant.

Cecily: It wouldn't have been a very serious engagement if it hadn't been broken off at least once. But I forgave you before the end of the week.

Algernon: What a perfect angel you are, Cecily.

Cecily: You dear romantic boy. *[He kisses her]*

Algernon: Do you promise that you'll never break off our engagement again, Cecily?

Cecily: I don't think I could break it off now that I have actually met you. Besides, of course, there is your name.

Algernon: *[Sounding nervous]* Yes, of course.

Cecily: You must not laugh at me, darling, but it had always been a dream of mine to love someone called Ernest. *[Algernon stands up and then Cecily does also]* There is something about that name which inspires confidence. I pity any poor married woman whose husband is not called Ernest.

Algernon: But, my dear child, couldn't you love me if I had another name?

Cecily: But what name?

Algernon: Oh, any name you like – Algernon – for instance …

Cecily: But I don't like the name Algernon.

Algernon: Well, my own dear, sweet, loving little darling, I can't see why you don't like the name Algernon. It is not a bad name. In fact, it is rather an aristocratic name. Half the fellows who get into the Bankruptcy Court[75] are called Algernon. But seriously, Cecily … *[Moving to her and making her sit down with him]* if my name was Algy, couldn't you love me?

Cecily: *[Standing up]* I might respect you, Ernest. I might admire your character, but I would not really want to spend very much time with you.

Algernon: Ahem! Cecily! *[Picking up his hat]* The clergyman here is, I suppose, a very experienced man?
Cecily: Oh, yes. Canon Chasuble is a very learned man. He has never written a single book, so you can imagine how much he knows.
Algernon: I must see him at once about an important baptism ... I mean ... on important business.
Cecily: Oh!
Algernon: I shan't be away for more than half an hour.
Cecily: We have been engaged since the fourteenth of February and I only met you today for the first time, so I think it is rather hard that you should leave me for as long as half an hour. Couldn't you make it twenty minutes?
Algernon: I'll be back in no time. *[He kisses her and runs down the garden]*
Cecily: What an impetuous boy he is! I must write about his proposal in my diary. *[She sits down and writes in her diary]*
[Merriman enters]
Merriman: A Miss Fairfax has just called to see Mr Worthing. She says it is on very important business.
Cecily: Isn't Mr Worthing in his library?
Merriman: Mr Worthing went to Canon Chasuble's house some time ago.
Cecily: Please ask the lady to come out into the garden and join me. Mr Worthing is sure to be back soon. And you can bring tea.
Merriman: Yes, miss.
[Merriman goes off]
Cecily: *[To herself]* Miss Fairfax! I suppose she is one of the many good women who help Uncle Jack with his charitable work in London. I don't really like women who are interested in charitable work. I think it is so presumptuous[76] of them.
[Merriman enters]
Merriman: Miss Fairfax.
[Gwendolen enters. Merriman goes off]

Cecily: *[Standing up and going to meet her]* Let me introduce myself to you. My name is Cecily Cardew.
Gwendolen: Cecily Cardew? *[Moving to her and shaking hands]* What a very sweet name! I think we are going to be great friends. I like you already more than I can say. My first impressions of people are never wrong.
Cecily: How nice of you to like me so much when we have known each other for such a short time. Please sit down.
Gwendolen: *[Still standing up]* I may call you Cecily, may I not?
Cecily: Of course, with pleasure.
Gwendolen: And you will always call me Gwendolen, won't you?
Cecily: If you wish.
Gwendolen: Then that is all quite settled, is it not?
Cecily: I hope so.
[A pause. Then they both sit down together]
Gwendolen: Perhaps this is a good opportunity to tell you who I am. My father is Lord Bracknell. You have never heard of Papa, I suppose?
Cecily: I don't think so.
Gwendolen: Outside the family circle, Papa, I am glad to say, is completely unknown. I think that is quite right. The home seems to me to be the proper place for a man. Certainly once a man begins to neglect his duties at home, it makes him very attractive. Cecily, Mama, whose views on education are very strict, has brought me up to be extremely short-sighted; it is part of her system. So do you mind me looking at you through my glasses?
Cecily: Oh! Not at all, Gwendolen. I like being looked at.
Gwendolen: *[After looking at Cecily carefully through a lorgnette[77]]* You are here on a short visit, I suppose?
Cecily: Oh no! I live here.
Gwendolen: *[Severely]* Really? Your mother, or an elderly female relation, lives here also?
Cecily: Oh no! I have no mother, nor, in fact, any relations.
Gwendolen: Indeed?

Cecily: My dear guardian, with the help of Miss Prism, has the difficult task of looking after me.
Gwendolen: Your guardian?
Cecily: Yes, I am Mr Worthing's ward.
Gwendolen: Oh! It is strange that he never mentioned to me that he had a ward. How secretive of him! He is becoming more interesting every hour. However, I am not sure that I am delighted by this news. *[Standing up and going to Cecily]* I have liked you ever since I met you, Cecily. But, now that I know you are Mr Worthing's ward, I must say that I wish you were – well – a bit older than you seem to be – and not quite so pretty. In fact, if I may speak candidly[78] ...
Cecily: Please do! I think that when one has anything unpleasant to say, one should always be quite candid.
Gwendolen: Well, to be quite candid, Cecily, I wish that you were at least forty-two years old and extremely plain. Ernest has an honourable, truthful nature. He would never be deceitful. But the most honourable men can be influenced by the beauty of others. Modern history, and indeed ancient history, give us many painful examples of what I refer to. Indeed, history would be quite unreadable if it were not so.
Cecily: I beg your pardon, Gwendolen, did you say 'Ernest'?
Gwendolen: Yes.
Cecily: Oh, but it is not Mr Ernest Worthing who is my guardian. It is his brother – his elder brother.
Gwendolen: *[Sitting down again]* Ernest never mentioned to me that he had a brother.
Cecily: I am sorry to say that they have not got on well with each other for a long time.
Gwendolen: Ah! I see. And now I think about it, I have never heard any man mention his brother. Most men don't seem to like the subject. Cecily, you have lifted a weight from my mind. I was becoming almost anxious. It would have been awful if any cloud had come across such a special friendship, would it not? Are you

quite, quite sure that it is not Mr Ernest Worthing who is your guardian?

Cecily: Quite sure. *[A pause]* In fact, I am going to be *his* guardian.

Gwendolen: I beg your pardon?

Cecily: *[Shyly]* Dearest Gwendolen, there is no reason why I should keep it a secret from you. It will be in the local newspaper next week. Mr Ernest Worthing and I are engaged to be married.

Gwendolen: *[Politely, standing up]* My darling Cecily, I think that there must be some small mistake. Mr Ernest Worthing is engaged to me. The announcement will appear in the newspapers on Saturday at the latest.

Cecily: *[Very politely, standing up]* I am afraid that you are mistaken. Ernest proposed to me exactly ten minutes ago. *[Showing her diary to Gwendolen]*

Gwendolen: *[Looking at the diary very carefully through her lorgnette]* It is very strange because he asked me to be his wife yesterday afternoon at half-past five. Please check for yourself. *[Producing a diary of her own]* I never travel without my diary. One should always have something exciting to read on the train. I am so sorry, dear Cecily, if it is any disappointment to you, but I am afraid that I was his first choice.

Cecily: It would make me very sad, dear Gwendolen, to cause you any pain, but I feel I must point out that since Ernest proposed to you he has clearly changed his mind.

Gwendolen: *[Thoughtfully]* If the poor fellow has been trapped into making a foolish promise, it is my duty to rescue him at once – and firmly.

Cecily: *[Thoughtfully and sadly]* If my dear boy has got into an unfortunate entanglement[79], I will never reproach[80] him for it when we are married.

Gwendolen: Are you calling me an entanglement, Miss Cardew? You are presumptuous. On an occasion of this kind, it becomes more than a duty to speak one's mind. It becomes a pleasure.

Cecily: Do you suggest, Miss Fairfax, that I trapped Ernest into

It is very strange because he asked me to be his wife yesterday afternoon.

an engagement? How dare you! This is no time to pretend to have good manners. When I see a spade, I call it a spade[P].

Gwendolen: I am glad to say that I have never seen a spade. It is obvious we do not live in the same social circle.

[Merriman enters, pushing a small trolley. It holds a tablecloth, a teapot, some milk, sugar, plates of cakes, muffins, teacake, bread and butter, and some plates. Cecily is about to reply but doesn't while the servant is there]

Merriman: Shall I set the table for afternoon tea here as usual, miss?

Cecily: *[Sternly, in a calm voice]* Yes, as usual. *[Merriman begins to lay the cloth on the table. There is a long pause. Cecily and Gwendolen look angrily at each other]*

Gwendolen: Are there many interesting walks near here, Miss Cardew?

Cecily: Oh, yes, a great many. From the top of one of the hills one can see five counties.

Gwendolen: Five counties! I don't think I should like that; I hate crowds.

Cecily: *[Sweetly]* I suppose that is why you live in town. *[Gwendolen doesn't answer and taps her foot nervously on the ground]*

Gwendolen: *[Looking around]* This is quite a well-kept garden, Miss Cardew.

Cecily: I'm glad you like it, Miss Fairfax.

Gwendolen: I had no idea there were any flowers in the country.

Cecily: Oh, flowers are as common here, Miss Fairfax, as people are in London.

Gwendolen: Personally, I cannot imagine how anyone manages to live in the country – if anybody who is anybody[P] does. The country always bores me to death[P].

Cecily: Would you like some tea, Miss Fairfax?

Gwendolen: *[Extremely politely]* Yes, thank you. *[To herself]* Hateful[81] girl! But I want some tea!

Cecily: *[Sweetly]* Sugar?

Gwendolen: No, thank you. Sugar is not fashionable anymore. *[Cecily looks angrily at her, picks up the sugar tongs*[82] *and puts four lumps of sugar into the cup]*

Cecily: *[Severely]* Cake or bread and butter?

Gwendolen: *[In a bored way]* Bread and butter, please. Cake is not seen in the best houses nowadays.

Cecily: *[Cutting a very large slice of cake and putting it on the tray which Merriman is holding]* Give that to Miss Fairfax.

[Merriman gives Gwendolen the cake and goes off. Gwendolen drinks some tea and makes a face. She puts down her cup, reaches out her hand for the bread and butter, looks at it and finds that it is cake. She stands up angrily]

Gwendolen: You have filled my tea with lumps of sugar. And, though I asked for bread and butter, you have given me cake. I am known to be sweet-tempered, but I warn you, Miss Cardew, you may go too far.

Cecily: *[Standing up]* I would go any distance to save my poor, innocent, trusting boy from being trapped by a girl like you.

Gwendolen: I have distrusted you from the moment I saw you. I felt you were false and deceitful. I am never wrong in such matters. My first impressions of people are always right.

Cecily: It seems to me that I am keeping you from other appointments. No doubt you have many other similar calls to make in the area.

[Jack enters]

Gwendolen: *[Seeing him]* Ernest! My own Ernest!

Jack: Gwendolen! Darling! *[Offering to kiss her]*

Gwendolen: *[Drawing away from Jack]* Wait a moment! May I ask if you are engaged to be married to this young lady? *[Pointing to Cecily]*

Jack: *[Laughing]* To dear little Cecily? Of course not! What could have put such an idea into your pretty little head?

Gwendolen: Thank you. You may kiss me. *[Offering her cheek]*

Cecily: *[Very sweetly]* I knew there must be some kind of

misunderstanding, Miss Fairfax. The gentleman whose arm is at present around your waist is my guardian, Mr Jack Worthing.
Gwendolen: I beg your pardon?
Cecily: This is Uncle Jack.
Gwendolen: *[Pulling away from Jack]* Jack! Oh!
[Algernon enters]
Cecily: *Here* is Ernest.
Algernon: *[Going straight to Cecily without noticing anyone else]* My own love! *[Offering to kiss her]*
Cecily: *[Drawing away from Algernon]* Wait a moment, Ernest! May I ask you – are you engaged to be married to this young lady?
Algernon: *[Looking around]* To what young lady? Good heavens! Gwendolen! Of course not! What could have put such an idea into your pretty little head?
Cecily: Thank you. *[Offering her cheek]* You may kiss me.
[Algernon kisses her]
Gwendolen: I felt there was some slight error, Miss Cardew. The gentleman whose arm is at present around your waist is my cousin, Mr Algernon Moncrieff.
Cecily: *[Breaking away from Algernon]* Algernon Moncrieff! Oh!
[The two girls move towards each other and put their arms around each other's waists as if for protection]
Are you called Algernon?
Algernon: I cannot deny it.
Cecily: Oh!
Gwendolen: Is your name really Jack?
Jack: *[Standing rather proudly]* I could deny it if I liked. I could deny anything if I liked. But my name certainly is Jack. It has been Jack for years.
Cecily: We have both been terribly deceived.
Gwendolen: My poor wounded Cecily!
Cecily: My poor wronged Gwendolen!
Gwendolen: *[Slowly and seriously]* Please will you call me 'sister'.
[They embrace. Jack and Algernon groan and walk up and down]

Are you called Algernon?

Cecily: *[Rather brightly]* There is just one question I would like to ask my guardian.
Gwendolen: A very good idea! Mr Worthing, there is just one question I would like permission to ask you. Where is your brother Ernest? We are both engaged to be married to your brother Ernest so it is important for us to know where he is at present.
Jack: *[Slowly and hesitantly]* Gwendolen – Cecily – it is very painful for me but I must speak the truth. It is the first time in my life that I have been in such a painful position and I am quite inexperienced at doing this. However, I will tell you honestly that I have no brother Ernest. I have no brother at all. I have never had a brother in my life and I don't intend ever to have a brother in the future.
Cecily: *[Surprised]* No brother at all?
Jack: *[Cheerfully]* None!
Gwendolen: *[Severely]* Did you ever have a brother of any kind?
Jack: *[Pleasantly]* Never. Not of any kind.
Gwendolen: I am afraid, Cecily, that neither of us is engaged to be married to anyone.
Cecily: It is not a very pleasant position for a young girl suddenly to find herself in, is it?
Gwendolen: Let us go into the house. They will not follow us into the house, will they?
Cecily: No, men are so cowardly[83], aren't they?
[They go into the house, after looking scornfully[84] at the men]
Jack: I suppose that this awful business is what you call Bunburying, is it?
Algernon: *[Laughing]* Yes, and it's the best Bunburying I have ever done in my life.
Jack: Well, you have no right to Bunbury here.
Algernon: That is absurd[85]. One has a right to Bunbury wherever one chooses. Every serious Bunburyist knows that.
Jack: What are you saying? Serious Bunburyist? Good heavens!
Algernon: Well, one must be serious about something if one

wants to enjoy one's life. I am serious about Bunburying. I have no idea what you are serious about – I suppose you are serious about everything.

Jack: Well, the only satisfaction I get from this awful business is that you won't be able to Bunbury anymore. Your friend, Bunbury, is quite finished. You won't be able to run away from town to the country quite so often now, Algy. And that's a very good thing.

Algernon: Your brother isn't very well, is he, Jack? Dead, in fact. You won't be able to run away to town from the country quite so often now. And that's a very good thing too.

Jack: And you have behaved very badly towards Miss Cardew. I must say that deceiving a sweet, simple girl like Cecily is very wicked of you. To say nothing of the fact[P] that she is my ward.

Algernon: I must say that deceiving a brilliant, clever young lady like Miss Fairfax is very wicked of you. To say nothing of the fact that she is my cousin.

Jack: I wanted to be engaged to Gwendolen, that is all. I love her.

Algernon: Well, I simply wanted to be engaged to Cecily. I adore her.

Jack: There is certainly no chance of you marrying Miss Cardew.

Algernon: I don't think there is much chance of you marrying Miss Fairfax, Jack. *[Sitting at the table and beginning to eat muffins]*

Jack: I can't understand how you can sit there calmly eating muffins when we are in this awful trouble. You seem to me to be perfectly heartless.

Algernon: Well, I can't eat muffins in an agitated[86] manner. The butter would probably get on my cuffs. One should always eat muffins calmly. It is the only way to eat them.

Jack: I think that it is perfectly heartless to be eating muffins at all in the circumstances.

Algernon: When I am in trouble, eating is the only thing which makes me feel better. Indeed, when I am in very great trouble, I refuse everything except food and drink. At present, I am eating

muffins because I am unhappy. Besides, I like muffins. *[Standing up]*
Jack: *[Standing up]* Well, that is no reason why you should eat them all. *[Taking the plate of muffins from Algernon]*
Algernon: *[Offering Jack teacake]* Please will you have teacake instead. I don't like teacake.
Jack: Good heavens! I think a man may eat his own muffins in his own garden.
Algernon: But you just said that it was perfectly heartless to eat muffins.
Jack: I said it was perfectly heartless of you to eat muffins. That is very different.
Algernon: Maybe. But the muffins are the same. *[Taking the plate of muffins from Jack]*
Jack: Algy, I wish you would go.
Algernon: You can't ask me to go without giving me some dinner. I never go without my dinner. Besides I have just arranged with Canon Chasuble to be baptized at a quarter to six. I am going to be baptized with the name of Ernest.
Jack: My dear fellow, no you aren't. That is nonsense. I arranged with Canon Chasuble to be baptized myself at half-past five. I will, of course, take the name Ernest. Gwendolen would want me to. We cannot both be baptized with the name Ernest. It's absurd. Besides, I have a right to be baptized if I like. There is no evidence that I have ever been baptized. I think it very likely that I never was and so does Canon Chasuble. It is different for you. You have been baptized already.
Algernon: Yes, but that was years ago.
Jack: Yes, but you have been baptized. That is the important thing.
Algernon: Yes indeed. So I know my health can bear it. I must say I think that it is rather dangerous for you to be baptized now. It might make you very unwell. You can't have forgotten that a close relative very nearly died in Paris this week of a bad cold.

Jack: Yes, but you said yourself that a bad cold was not hereditary.
Algernon: I know it didn't use to be – but it probably is now. Science is always making wonderful improvements.
Jack: *[Picking up the muffin plate]* Oh that is nonsense. You always talk nonsense.
Algernon: Jack – muffins again! I wish you wouldn't. There are only two left. *[Taking them]* I told you I was particularly fond of muffins.
Jack: But I hate teacake.
Algernon: Then why on earth do you serve teacake to your guests? I don't like your ideas of hospitality.
Jack: Algernon! I have already told you to go. I don't want you here. Why don't you go?
Algernon: Because I haven't finished my tea yet! I have one muffin left.
[Jack groans and sits down. Algernon continues eating]

Act Three

[The living room at the Manor House. Gwendolen and Cecily are at the window looking out into the garden]

Gwendolen: They have not followed us into the house, as anyone else would have done. They must be ashamed.

Cecily: They have been eating muffins. That looks like repentance to me.

Gwendolen: *[After a pause while she thinks about what Cecily has said]* They don't seem to notice us at all. Couldn't you cough?

Cecily: But I haven't got a cough.

Gwendolen: They're looking at us. How dare they!

Cecily: They're coming towards us. How presumptuous of them.

Gwendolen: Let us remain silent and dignified.

Cecily: Certainly. It is the only thing to do now.

[Jack enters, followed by Algernon. They are whistling the tune of a popular song]

Gwendolen: This dignified silence is rather unpleasant.

Cecily: Yes, I agree. It is.

Gwendolen: But we will not be the first to speak.

Cecily: Certainly not.

Gwendolen: Mr Worthing, I have something to ask you. Your reply is extremely important.

Cecily: Gwendolen, I value your common sense. Mr Moncrieff, I would be grateful if you would answer the following question. Why did you pretend to be my guardian's brother?

Algernon: In order that I might have the opportunity of meeting you.

Cecily: *[To Gwendolen]* That seems a satisfactory explanation, does it not?

Gwendolen: Yes, dear, if you can believe him.

Cecily: I don't believe him. But it is a wonderful answer.

Gwendolen: That is true. If you are talking about something very serious, the style of what you say is much more important than the sincerity. Mr Worthing, why did you pretend to have a brother? Was it in order that you could come to town as often as possible to see me?

Jack: Can you doubt that, Miss Fairfax?

Gwendolen: I have very strong doubts. But I intend to ignore them. *[Going closer to Cecily]* Their explanations appear to be quite satisfactory, especially Mr Worthing's. His answer seems to me to be particularly truthful.

Cecily: I am very happy with what Mr Moncrieff said. The sound of his voice alone makes me feel certain that I should believe him.

Gwendolen: Then, do you think we should forgive them?

Cecily: Yes … I mean no.

Gwendolen: I agree! I had forgotten something. We have ideals which we must not ignore. Which of us should tell them? The task is not a pleasant one.

Cecily: Could we not both speak to them at the same time?

Gwendolen: That is an excellent idea! I nearly always speak at the same time as other people. Are you ready?

Cecily: Certainly.

[Gwendolen beats time with a finger as if she is conducting an orchestra]

Gwendolen and Cecily: *[Speaking together]* Your first names are a problem that cannot be solved. That is all!

Jack and Algernon: *[Speaking together]* Our first names! Is that all? But we are going to be baptized later this afternoon.

Gwendolen: *[To Jack]* Are you really prepared to do this terrible thing for my sake?

Jack: I am.

Cecily: *[To Algernon]* Are you really prepared to face this awful ordeal[87] to please me?

Algernon: I am!

Gwendolen: How absurd to talk about the equality of the sexes! Men are infinitely[88] better than us at self-sacrifice.

Jack: We are! *[Getting hold of Algernon's hand]*

Cecily: They have moments of courage of which we women know nothing.
Gwendolen: *[To Jack]* Darling!
Cecily: *[To Algernon]* Darling!
[They fall into each other's arms. Merriman enters. When he sees the situation, he coughs loudly]
Merriman: Ahem! Ahem! Lady Bracknell is here.
Jack: Good heavens!
[Lady Bracknell enters. The couples separate very quickly. Merriman goes off]
Lady Bracknell: Gwendolen! What does this mean?
Gwendolen: It means that I am engaged to be married to Mr Worthing, Mama.
Lady Bracknell: Come here. Sit down. Sit down immediately. *[To Jack]* I learnt of Gwendolen's sudden departure from her trusted maid, who gave me the information after I had given her a small coin. I followed her at once on the next train. Her father does not know where she is and I don't propose to tell him the truth. In fact, I never tell him the truth about anything. I would consider it wrong to do so. You must understand that all communication between you and my daughter must stop immediately. On this point, as indeed on all points, I am firm.
Jack: I am engaged to be married to Gwendolen, Lady Bracknell!
Lady Bracknell: You are not, sir. And now ... Algernon! ...
Algernon: Yes, Aunt Augusta.
Lady Bracknell: Is this the house in which your invalid friend Mr Bunbury lives?
Algernon: *[Finding it difficult to speak]* Oh! No! Bunbury doesn't live here. Bunbury is somewhere else at present. In fact, Bunbury is dead.
Lady Bracknell: Dead! When did Mr Bunbury die? His death must have been extremely sudden.
Algernon: Oh! I killed Bunbury this afternoon ... I mean poor Bunbury died this afternoon.

Gwendolen! What does this mean?

Lady Bracknell: What did he die of?
Algernon: Bunbury? Oh he was quite exploded[89].
Lady Bracknell: Exploded? Was he the victim of a terrorist plot? I was not aware that Mr Bunbury was interested in politics. If so, he deserved his punishment.
Algernon: My dear Aunt Augusta, I mean that he was found out! What I mean is the doctors found out that Bunbury could not live – so he died.
Lady Bracknell: He seems to have had great confidence in his doctors' opinions. I am glad, however, that he made up his mind to do something definite and acted on proper medical advice. And now, Mr Worthing, may I ask: who is that young person whose hand my nephew Algernon is holding? He is holding it, I may add, in a most unnecessary way.
Jack: The lady is Miss Cecily Cardew, my ward. *[Lady Bracknell bows coldly to Cecily]*
Algernon: I am engaged to be married to Cecily, Aunt Augusta.
Lady Bracknell: I beg your pardon?
Cecily: Mr Moncrieff and I are engaged to be married, Lady Bracknell.
Lady Bracknell: *[Shivering, then moving over to the sofa and sitting down]* I do not know whether there is anything very exciting about the air in Hertfordshire, but the number of engagements being made seems to be considerably above the expected average. I think that it would be a good idea for me to make some preliminary enquiries. Mr Worthing, is Miss Cardew connected with any of the larger railway stations in London? I am merely asking for information. I did not know until yesterday that there were families or persons who were related to railway stations.
Jack: *[Speaking in a cold, clear voice]* Miss Cardew is the granddaughter of the late Mr Thomas Cardew of 149 Belgrave Square, London; of Gervase Park, Dorking, Surrey; and also of The Sporran, Fifeshire, Scotland.
Lady Bracknell: That sounds not unsatisfactory. Three addresses

always inspire confidence. But I have no proof that they are real.
Jack: Miss Cardew's family lawyers are Markby, Markby and Markby.
Lady Bracknell: Markby, Markby and Markby? They are lawyers in the very highest position of their profession. Indeed I know that one of the Mr Markbys is occasionally to be seen at dinner parties. I am almost satisfied.
Jack: *[Very irritably]* How extremely kind of you, Lady Bracknell! I have also got, you will be pleased to hear, certificates of Miss Cardew's birth, baptism and confirmation of vaccinations for whooping cough[90] and the measles[91] – both German and English.
Lady Bracknell: Ah! A busy life, I see. Though perhaps it has been too exciting for a young girl. I do not believe a young girl should have too many experiences. *[Standing up and looking at her watch]* Gwendolen! We must leave. We have not a moment to lose. Since I am making enquiries, Mr Worthing, I had better ask you if Miss Cardew has any personal fortune.
Jack: Oh! She has an investment of a hundred and thirty thousand pounds in Government Stocks[92], so her annual income is very large. That is all. Goodbye, Lady Bracknell. So pleased to have seen you.
Lady Bracknell: *[Sitting down again]* Just a moment, Mr Worthing. A hundred and thirty thousand pounds! And in Government Stocks! Miss Cardew seems to me to be a very attractive young lady, now that I look at her. Few girls today have any good qualities which last and improve with time. We live in a time, sadly, when beauty is the only important thing. *[To Cecily]* Come here, dear. *[Cecily goes to her]* You are a pretty child! Your dress is not very fashionable and your hair has not been styled very well. But we can soon alter that. An experienced French maid will produce a very good result in a short time. I remember recommending one to Lady Lancing and after a few months her own husband did not know her.
Jack: After a few months nobody knew her.

Lady Bracknell: *[Glaring at Jack, then pretending to smile at Cecily]* Turn round, sweet child. *[Cecily turns completely round in a circle]* No, I want to see you from the side. *[Cecily turns round so that Lady Bracknell can see her face in profile from the side]* Yes, very good. There is much about your situation which is promising – you could fit well into good society. Hold your chin a little higher, dear. Chins are worn very high at present. Algernon!
Algernon: Yes, Aunt Augusta!
Lady Bracknell: There is much about her situation which is promising – she could fit well into good society.
Algernon: Cecily is the sweetest, dearest, prettiest girl in the whole world. And I don't care about her fitting into good society.
Lady Bracknell: Do not be dismissive of good society, Algernon. Only people who can't get into good society speak like that. *[To Cecily]* Dear child, of course Algernon has no money. He has nothing but his debts to bring to a marriage. But I do not approve of marrying for money. When I married Lord Bracknell, I had no fortune at all, but I didn't allow that to stand in my way[p]. Well, I suppose I must give my consent to this marriage.
Algernon: Thank you, Aunt Augusta.
Lady Bracknell: Cecily, you may kiss me!
Cecily: *[Kissing her]* Thank you, Lady Bracknell.
Lady Bracknell: You may also call me Aunt Augusta in future.
Cecily: Thank you, Aunt Augusta.
Lady Bracknell: The marriage ought to take place quite soon.
Algernon: Thank you, Aunt Augusta.
Cecily: Thank you, Aunt Augusta.
Lady Bracknell: I do not approve of long engagements. They give people a chance to find out about each other's character before marriage, which I think is never advisable.
Jack: I beg your pardon, Lady Bracknell, but their engagement is not acceptable. I am Miss Cardew's guardian and she cannot marry without my consent until she comes of age[p]. I will not give my consent.

Lady Bracknell: Why, may I ask? Algernon is an extremely eligible young man. He has nothing, but he looks as if he has everything. What more can one want?
Jack: I am very sorry to have to say this to you, Lady Bracknell, but the fact is that I do not approve of his character. I suspect that he is devious.
[Algernon and Cecily look at him, amazed and indignant[93]*]*
Lady Bracknell: Devious? My nephew Algernon? Impossible! He was educated at Oxford University.
Jack: There can be no doubt about it. This afternoon, while I was away in London, he was allowed into this house because he said he was my brother. While pretending to be my brother, he drank, I am informed by my servant, a complete bottle of very good quality champagne which I was keeping especially for myself. He also succeeded in turning my ward against me. He then stayed to tea and ate every muffin we had. He behaved completely heartlessly. And what is worse, he knew that I don't have a brother, that I have never had a brother and that I don't intend to ever have a brother of any kind. He knew because I told him so myself yesterday afternoon.
Lady Bracknell: *[Coughing]* Ahem! Mr Worthing, after thinking about this carefully, I have decided to forget about the way my nephew behaved towards you.
Jack: That is very good of you, Lady Bracknell. I have decided, however, not to change my mind. I will not give my consent.
Lady Bracknell: *[To Cecily]* Come here, sweet child. *[Cecily goes to her]* How old are you, my dear?
Cecily: Well, I am really only eighteen, but I always say I am twenty when I go to parties.
Lady Bracknell: You are perfectly right to make a small alteration. Indeed, no woman should ever be quite accurate about her age. It looks so devious. *[Speaking again, thoughtfully]* Well, it will not be very long before you come of age. So I don't think your guardian's consent is very important.

Jack: Excuse me for interrupting you again, Lady Bracknell. I must tell you that, according to her grandfather's will, Miss Cardew does not come of age until she is thirty-five.
Lady Bracknell: That does not seem to me to be a problem. Thirty-five is a very attractive age. London society is full of women who have, by their own free choice, remained thirty-five for years. Lady Dumbleton is an example. She has been thirty-five ever since she reached the age of forty, which was many years ago. Our dear Cecily will be even more attractive at the age of thirty-five than she is at present. She will have even more money then than she has now.
Cecily: Algy, could you wait for me till I was thirty-five?
Algernon: Of course I could, Cecily. You know I could.
Cecily: Yes, I believe that you could, but I couldn't wait all that time. I hate waiting even five minutes for anybody. It always makes me rather cross. I am not punctual myself but I do like other people to be punctual. Waiting, even to be married, is quite out of the question[P].
Algernon: Then what are we going to do, Cecily?
Cecily: I don't know, Mr Moncrieff.
Lady Bracknell: My dear Mr Worthing, Miss Cardew states that she cannot wait till she is thirty-five – a remark that tells me she has a rather impatient nature – however, I beg of you to think again about your decision.
Jack: My dear Lady Bracknell, the decision is entirely in your own hands[P]. When you consent to my marriage with Gwendolen, I will gladly consent to your nephew's marriage with my ward.
Lady Bracknell: *[Standing and looking very tall]* You must know that your marriage with my daughter is not possible.
Jack: Then none of us can look forward to ever getting married.
Lady Bracknell: I cannot agree to Gwendolen never getting married. Algernon, of course, may choose for himself. Come, dear, *[Gwendolen stands up]* we have already missed five, if not six, trains. *[Canon Chasuble enters]*

Chasuble: Everything is quite ready for the baptisms.
Lady Bracknell: The baptisms? Is it not a little early for baptisms? First marriage, then children, *then* baptisms!
Chasuble: *[Looking puzzled and pointing at Jack and Algernon]* Both these gentlemen have said they wish to be baptized immediately.
Lady Bracknell: Baptized? At their age? The idea is ridiculous and quite irreligious. Algernon, I forbid you to be baptized. My husband, Lord Bracknell, would be very displeased to hear that you were wasting your time and money like this.
Chasuble: Do I understand you correctly? Is neither of you gentlemen to be baptized?
Jack: I don't think that baptism would be much use to either of us at the moment, Canon Chasuble.
Chasuble: I am very sorry to hear you say so, Mr Worthing. That sounds like the view of an irreligious man. I have written four unpublished sermons on this subject. However, since you have decided to ignore religion for now, I will return to the church where Miss Prism has been waiting for me for an hour and a half.
Lady Bracknell: *[Looking shocked and sitting down again]* Miss Prism? Did I hear you say 'Miss Prism'?
Chasuble: Yes, Lady Bracknell. I am going to the church to join her now.
Lady Bracknell: Please wait a moment, Canon Chasuble. This is something which may be important to Lord Bracknell and myself. Is this Miss Prism a rather ugly female who is remotely connected with education?
Chasuble: *[Rather indignantly]* She is a very respectable lady.
Lady Bracknell: It must be the same person. May I ask what position she has in your household?
Chasuble: *[Severely]* I am celibate[94], madam.
Jack: Lady Bracknell, Miss Prism has been Miss Cardew's valued governess and companion for the last three years.
Lady Bracknell: I must see her at once. Let her be sent for.
Chasuble: *[Looking offstage]* She's approaching. She's nearly here.

[Miss Prism enters very quickly]
Miss Prism: I was told you were coming to the church, dear canon. I have been waiting there for an hour and three-quarters. *[Seeing Lady Bracknell, who is glaring at her, Miss Prism turns pale. She looks round her as if she wants to escape]*
Lady Bracknell: *[In a severe voice, as if she is a lawyer in a courtroom]* Prism! *[Miss Prism lowers her head, looking ashamed]* Come here, Prism! *[Miss Prism approaches looking nervous]* Prism! Where is that baby? *[Everyone looks horrified. The canon takes a step backwards. Algernon and Jack pretend to be anxious to stop Gwendolen and Cecily from hearing something shocking]* Prism, twenty-eight years ago, you left Lord Bracknell's house, Number 104, Upper Grosvenor Square, London, in charge of a pram[95] containing a baby boy. You never returned. A few weeks later, after a police investigation, the pram was discovered at midnight in a remote part of the city. It contained the manuscript of a very bad three-volume novel. *[Miss Prism looks indignant]* But the baby was not there. *[Everyone looks at Miss Prism]* Prism, where is that baby? *[There is a pause]*
Miss Prism: Lady Bracknell, I am ashamed to say I don't know. I wish I did. These are the facts. On the morning of that day, a day I will remember forever, I prepared as usual to take the baby out in the pram. I had with me a large old handbag in which I had intended to put the manuscript of a three-volume novel that I had written. In a moment of forgetfulness, for which I can never forgive myself, I put the manuscript in the pram and the baby in the handbag.
Jack: *[Who had been listening very carefully]* But where did you put the handbag?
Miss Prism: Do not ask me, Mr Worthing.
Jack: Miss Prism, this is very important to me. I must know where you put the handbag which contained the baby.
Miss Prism: I left it in the cloakroom of one of the larger railway stations in London.

I put the manuscript in the pram and the baby in the handbag.

Jack: Which railway station?
Miss Prism: *[Looking very miserable]* Victoria. *[Sitting down slowly on an armchair]*
Jack: I must go to my bedroom for a moment. Gwendolen, wait for me here.
Gwendolen: If you are not too long, I will wait for you all my life. *[Jack leaves, very excited]*
Chasuble: What do you think this means, Lady Bracknell?
Lady Bracknell: I dare not guess, Canon Chasuble. You must know that strange coincidences are not supposed to happen in families with a high position in society like ours. They are not appropriate.
[Noises are heard above as if someone is throwing boxes around. Everyone looks up]
Cecily: Uncle Jack sounds very agitated.
Lady Bracknell: The noise is extremely unpleasant.
Chasuble: *[Looking up]* It has stopped now. *[The noises start again, sounding even louder]*
Lady Bracknell: I wish he would stop.
Gwendolen: The suspense is terrible. I hope it will last.
[Jack enters, with a black leather handbag in his hand]
Jack: *[Rushing over to Miss Prism]* Is this the handbag, Miss Prism? Examine it carefully before you speak. The happiness of more than one person depends on your answer.
Miss Prism: *[Calmly]* It seems to be mine. Yes, here is the damage which happened in an accident on a bus. Here is the stain caused by a drink which exploded at Leamington. And here, near the lock, are my initials. I had forgotten that I had had them put there. The bag is definitely mine. I am delighted to have it returned to me so unexpectedly. It has been inconvenient not to have it all these years.
Jack: *[In a pathetic voice]* Miss Prism, you have had more returned to you than the handbag. I was the baby you placed in it.
Miss Prism: *[Amazed]* You?

Jack: *[Embracing her]* Yes … Mother!

Miss Prism: *[Pulling away from him indignantly]* Mr Worthing, I am unmarried.

Jack: Unmarried! That is a serious problem. But who has the right to speak badly of someone who has suffered? Why should society treat men and women differently? Mother, I forgive you. *[Trying to embrace her again]*

Miss Prism: *[Now even more indignant]* Mr Worthing, you are wrong. *[Pointing to Lady Bracknell]* There is the lady who can tell you who you really are.

Jack: *[After a pause]* Lady Bracknell, would you kindly inform me who I am?

Lady Bracknell: I am afraid that my news may not please you. You are the son of my poor sister, Mrs Moncrieff, and therefore Algernon's elder brother.

Jack: Algy's elder brother! Then I have a brother after all. I knew I had a brother! I always said I had a brother! Cecily – how could you ever have doubted that I had a brother? *[Getting hold of Algernon and leading him around the room]* Canon Chasuble, here is my unfortunate brother. Miss Prism, my unfortunate brother. Gwendolen, my unfortunate brother. Algy, you will have to treat me with more respect in the future. You have never behaved to me like a younger brother should.

Algernon: Well, I haven't done until today. I did my best, though. *[They shake hands]*

Gwendolen: *[To Jack]* My own – but my own – what? What is your name, now that you are not Jack Worthing?

Jack: Good heavens! I had forgotten about my name. I suppose that you won't change your mind about your favourite name?

Gwendolen: Never!

Jack: Then the question must be cleared up at once. Aunt Augusta, had I been baptized?

Lady Bracknell: Your loving parents had done everything for you, including baptism.

Jack: Then I was baptized! That is clear. Now what name was I given? Let me know the worst!
Lady Bracknell: You were the elder son so you were given your father's name.
Jack: *[Irritably]* Yes, but what was my father's name?
Lady Bracknell: *[Thoughtfully]* I cannot at present remember what the general's name was. But I have no doubt that he had one.
Jack: Algy! Can't you remember what our father's name was?
Algernon: My dear fellow, we never even spoke to each other. He died before I was a year old.
Jack: His name will appear in the Army Lists[96] of that period, I suppose, Aunt Augusta?
Lady Bracknell: The general was a man of peace, except in his domestic life. So I have no doubt that his name will appear in an Army List.
Jack: The Army Lists for the last forty years are here. I should have read them all! *[Rushes over to a bookcase and pulls lots of books out]* Mmm ... generals ... Mallam, Maxbohm, Magley – what awful names they have – Markby, Migsby, Mobbs, Moncrieff! Lieutenant: 1840, Captain, Lieutenant-Colonel, Colonel, General: 1869: names Ernest John. *[Putting down the book and speaking quite calmly]* I always told you, Gwendolen, that my name was Ernest, didn't I? Well, it *is* Ernest after all. I mean it really is Ernest.
Lady Bracknell: Yes, I remember now that the general called you Ernest. I knew I had a reason for disliking that name.
Gwendolen: Ernest! My own Ernest! I felt from the first time I met you that you could have no other name!
Jack: Gwendolen, it is terrible for a man to find out suddenly that he has been speaking the truth all his life. Can you forgive me?
Gwendolen: I can. Because I feel that you are going to change.
Jack: My own darling!

I always told you, Gwendolen, that my name was Ernest, didn't I?

Chasuble: *[To Miss Prism]* Laetitia! *[Embracing her]*
Miss Prism: *[Enthusiastically]* Frederick! At last!
Algernon: Cecily! *[Embracing her]* At last!
Jack: Gwendolen! *[Embracing her]* At last!
Lady Bracknell: My nephew, you seem to be displaying signs of a lack of seriousness.
Jack: On the contrary, Aunt Augusta, I've now realized for the first time in my life the Importance of Being Earnest.

Points for Understanding

Act One

1 Algernon discusses marriage with Jack. When he says that 'divorces are made in Heaven', he is inverting the sense of an old English proverb: 'marriages are made in Heaven'. Can you find another saying of Algernon's later in the act which you think might be an inverted proverb? Do you know, or can you guess, what the original form of this proverb is?

2 'It is very impolite to read a private cigarette case!' Jack tells Algernon. Explain why this is a joke.

3 'My dear fellow, some aunts are tall. Some aunts are not tall. My aunt should be allowed to decide her height for herself,' Jack tells Algernon. Explain why he says this.

4 'To lose one parent, Mr Worthing, is unfortunate; to lose both seems like carelessness,' says Lady Bracknell. Explain her deliberate misunderstanding of what Jack has just told her.

5 Algernon tells Jack that he should claim that his brother has died of a bad cold. Wilde has chosen this illness deliberately because it is a comical one. What is comical about it?

Act Two

1 Near the beginning of the act, Canon Chasuble says to Cecily, 'If I was Miss Prism's pupil, I would always pay attention.' And later Miss Prism tells the canon that if a man has a wife who is a mature woman, 'she can be relied upon'. What future development is hinted at in these speeches?

2 When Jack announces the death of his brother, Miss Prism says, 'What a lesson for him! I hope he will learn from this.' What is Wilde telling his audience about the character of the governess when he makes this joke?

3 Canon Chasuble says that he will preach a sermon which will mention Jack's brother's death. He has already got a sermon that 'can be used on any occasion, happy or sad'. He adds, 'I have preached it at baptisms, weddings and funerals.' What is Wilde really telling us about this sermon?
4 'I haven't got a brother,' Jack says when Cecily tells him that his brother Ernest has arrived at the house. Cecily and Canon Chasuble understand what Jack says in different ways. Explain why.
5 Both Gwendolen and Cecily keep diaries. What do we learn about the characters of the girls from the reasons they give for keeping diaries?
6 Gwendolen and Cecily conclude at one point in the act that they are both engaged to the same man. Explain briefly how this has happened.
7 The conversation between Gwendolen and Cecily on the subject of flowers seems polite but they are really insulting each other. Explain how.
8 How, according to Algernon, does a wonderful improvement in science make it dangerous for Jack to be baptized? How sensible is Algernon's suggestion?

Act Three

1 On her entrance Lady Bracknell refers to Gwendolen's 'trusted' maid. This expression is a cliché from the period when the play was written, but why is Lady Bracknell's use of it here ironic?
2 'Is Miss Cardew connected with any of the larger railway stations in London?' Lady Bracknell asks. What does she really mean?
3 'Few girls today have any good qualities which last and improve with time,' Lady Bracknell says. But she obviously regards Cecily as an exception. Why?
4 When Miss Prism is shown the handbag in which Jack was found, her reaction is an example of 'bathos' – a sudden change from seriousness to triviality. Explain why.

Glossary

1 ***salon*** (page 4)
in the past, a regular meeting of artists, writers, musicians etc, usually at the home of a rich, famous woman

2 ***aesthetics*** (page 4)
the study of the nature of beauty, especially in arts such as painting and architecture

3 ***influenced*** – *to influence someone* (page 4)
to affect the way that someone thinks or behaves, or to affect the way that something happens

4 ***infamous*** (page 4)
well known for something bad

5 ***decadent*** (page 4)
describing or involving a lot of pleasure that is considered immoral. A person who is *decadent* allows himself or herself so much pleasure that it almost seems morally wrong.

6 ***satirized*** – *to satirize* (page 5)
to use humour to criticize someone or something and make them seem silly. This use of humour is called *satire* and someone who uses this type of humour is a *satirist*.

7 ***epigram*** (page 5)
a short poem or sentence that expresses something such as a feeling or idea in a short and clever or funny way

8 ***trivial*** (page 6)
not very important, serious or valuable

9 ***impending*** (page 6)
an *impending* event or situation, especially an unpleasant one, is one that will happen very soon

10 ***Victorian*** (page 6)
relating to the period from 1837 to 1901, when Queen Victoria ruled the UK. In this period, upper-class people had very strict moral attitudes.

11 ***sub-plot*** (page 6)
a story in a play, novel or film that is separate from the main story and is not as important as the main story

12 ***subversive*** (page 6)
intended to destroy the power or influence of a government or an established belief

13 ***inversion*** (page 6)
the process of changing something to make it the opposite of what it was before, or turning it upside down

14 ***cynical*** (page 7)
someone who is *cynical* believes that people care only about themselves and are not sincere or honest. This belief is called *cynicism*.

15 ***deviousness*** (page 7)
the quality of being *devious* – dishonest and clever

16 ***alters*** – *to alter something* (page 7)
to make something or someone different

17 ***meek*** (page 7)
quiet, gentle and easily persuaded by other people to do what they want

18 ***fiancé*** (page 7)
someone's *fiancé* is the man they are engaged to and are going to get married to. The woman someone is engaged to and is going to get married to is their *fiancée*.

19 ***repentance*** (page 8)
the act of showing that you feel ashamed and sorry because you recognize that you have done something wrong, especially against the rules of your religion

20 ***deceived*** – *to deceive someone* (page 8)
to trick someone by behaving in a dishonest way. Someone who *deceives* people is *deceitful*.

21 ***muffin*** (page 8)
a flat round type of bread, usually cut in half and eaten hot with butter. *Muffins* are often part of afternoon tea. People also eat *crumpets* with afternoon tea. *Crumpets* are a flat round cake, also eaten hot with butter. Another type of cake that people eat with afternoon tea is a *teacake*. *Teacakes* are a type of small round cake with raisins – dried grapes – in them.

22 ***sums up*** – *to sum up* (page 8)
to make a statement that shows what something or someone is like

23 ***aristocratic*** (page 8)
belonging to or typical of the *aristocracy* – the people in the highest class of society, who usually have money, land and power and who often have special titles, such as 'duke' or 'countess'

24 ***season*** (page 8)
a period of the year when a series of special events for fashionable, upper-class society take place

25 ***eligible*** (page 9)
considered to be suitable as a marriage partner because you are rich or attractive

26 ***bachelor*** (page 10)
a man who has never been married. An *eligible bachelor* is one who many women want to marry because he is rich or attractive. A woman who is not married and is past the age when women usually get married is called a *spinster*. *Spinster* is an old-fashioned and insulting word. Now, it is more usual to say that a man or woman who is not married is *single*.

27 ***ward*** (page 10)
someone, especially a child, who is officially being looked after by a court of law or by someone who is not their parents. The person who looks after them is their *guardian*.

28 ***governess*** (page 10)
a woman whose job is to look after and teach her employer's children in their home, especially in the past

29 ***Canon*** (page 10)
a Christian priest who works in a cathedral

30 ***misunderstanding*** (page 11)
a failure to understand someone or something correctly

31 ***morals*** (page 11)
principles of right or wrong behaviour that are generally accepted by a society

32 ***Shropshire*** (page 12)
a *county* – a region that has its own local government – on the west coast of England. *Shropshire* has more countryside and fewer inhabitants than most other regions in England.

33 ***fellow*** (page 12)
used for talking to a man in an old-fashioned, friendly way

34 ***extravagant*** (page 12)
spending or costing a lot of money, especially more than is reasonable

35 ***flirt*** – *to flirt with someone* (page 12)
to behave towards someone in a way that shows your sexual or romantic interest in them

36 ***consent*** (page 13)
permission to do something

37 ***clear up*** – *to clear up something* (page 15)
to solve a problem or a mystery

38 ***inscription*** (page 15)
a piece of writing written or cut on or in something, especially as a record of an achievement or in order to honour someone

39 ***visiting card*** (page 16)
a small card with your name printed on it that people left in the past with people who they visited

40 ***quite*** (page 16)
quite usually means to some degree, but not completely or extremely, but speakers of British English sometimes use *quite* to mean 'very'. This is only possible before words with an extreme meaning. When Algernon says that he is *quite* sure, he means that he is very sure.

41 ***will*** (page 17)
a legal document that explains what you want to happen to your money and possessions after you die. This is often more formally called a *last will and testament*.

42 ***invalid*** (page 18)
someone who is ill or injured and is unable to look after themselves

43 ***frowning*** – *to frown* (page 20)
to move your eyebrows down and closer together because you are annoyed, worried or thinking hard

44 ***telegram*** (page 20)
a message that you send by *telegraph* – a method of communicating by sending electric signals through wires or by radio waves – used especially in the past for short urgent messages

45 ***reception*** (page 22)
a formal party to welcome someone or to celebrate something

46 ***ideal*** (page 22)
the best example of something that you can think of or imagine

47 ***baptized*** – *to baptize someone* (page 23)
to perform a religious ceremony during which a baby is made a member of the Christian religion and given a name

48 ***carriage*** (page 24)
a vehicle with wheels that is pulled by horses, especially one used in the past before cars were invented

49 ***occupation*** (page 25)
something that you do in your free time. A more usual meaning of *occupation* is job.

50 ***investment*** (page 25)
money used in a way that may earn you more money, for example money used for buying property or shares in a company

51 ***late*** (page 26)
used for talking about someone who has died, especially recently

52 ***cloakroom*** (page 27)
a room in a theatre, station etc where people can leave their coats, bags and other possessions while they are in the building

53 ***dignity*** (page 27)
the impressive behaviour of someone who controls their emotions in a difficult situation. If someone behaves in this way, people say that they are *dignified*.

54 ***Wedding March*** (page 27)
a piece of music traditionally played when a woman arrives at her wedding or when she and her husband leave after it

55 ***hereditary*** (page 29)
a *hereditary* disease or quality is passed from a parent to a child in their genes

56 ***Club*** (page 29)
an organization that provides a place where its members, especially men, can go and eat, relax or stay

57 ***Music Hall*** (page 29)
a type of entertainment of the late nineteenth and early twentieth centuries that consisted of a series of short performances by singers, dancers and comedians in a theatre

58 ***cuff*** (page 30)
the part of a sleeve that fits around your wrist

59 ***impetuous*** (page 32)
done quickly, without thinking about what the effects will be

60 ***dismissive*** (page 35)
reacting to something in a way that shows you do not think it is worth paying attention to

61 ***housekeeper*** (page 37)
someone whose job is to organize all the work that needs to be done in someone's house, such as cleaning, cooking etc

62 ***hypocrisy*** (page 37)
behaviour in which someone claims to have certain moral principles or beliefs but behaves in a way that shows they are not sincere

63 ***reform*** – *to reform someone* (page 38)
to change your own or someone else's behaviour so that it is no longer illegal or harmful

64 ***mourning clothes*** (page 39)
clothes, especially black clothes, that are worn as a sign of respect for someone who has died

65 ***condolences*** (page 40)
the things that you say to show sympathy when someone has just died

66 ***charity*** (page 40)
kindness that you show towards other people by not judging them or criticizing them too severely. *Charity* is more usually used to talk about money or food that is given to people who are poor or ill so that they can live.

67 ***draught*** (page 40)
cold air that blows into a room and makes you feel uncomfortable

68 ***sermon*** (page 40)
a speech made by a priest or religious leader, especially as part of a religious ceremony

69 ***discontent*** (page 40)
the unhappy feeling that you have when you are not satisfied with something

70 ***bitterly*** (page 41)
in a way that shows that you are extremely angry, upset or disappointed about something

71 **glares** – *to glare at someone or something* (page 42)
to look at someone or something in a very angry way

72 ***reconciliation*** (page 44)
a new and friendly relationship with someone who you argued with or fought with

73 ***scoundrel*** (page 44)
an old-fashioned word for a man who behaves in an unfair or dishonest way

74 ***conceited*** (page 49)
someone who is *conceited* behaves in a way that shows they think they are very intelligent, skilful or attractive

75 ***Bankruptcy Court*** (page 50)
a person or business that is *bankrupt* has officially admitted that they have no money and cannot pay what they owe. The situation of being *bankrupt* is called *bankruptcy*. People who are *bankrupt* must attend a *court* – a place where trials take place and legal cases are decided. Algernon is saying that a lot of people who owe money and cannot pay are called Algernon.

76 ***presumptuous*** (page 51)
showing too much confidence and not enough respect
77 ***lorgnette*** (page 52)
old-fashioned glasses with a long handle that you hold in front of your eyes
78 ***candidly*** (page 53)
speaking in an honest and direct way, even when the truth is not pleasant
79 ***entanglement*** (page 54)
a complicated situation or relationship
80 ***reproach*** – *to reproach someone for (doing) something* (page 54)
to criticize someone and feel disappointed with them for something they have done
81 ***hateful*** (page 56)
extremely bad, unpleasant or cruel
82 ***sugar tongs*** (page 57)
a metal or plastic object that consists of two connected arms that you push together in order to pick up lumps of sugar
83 ***cowardly*** (page 60)
a *cowardly* person is not brave enough to fight or do something difficult or dangerous that they should do
84 ***scornfully*** (page 60)
in a way that shows you do not think someone or something is good enough to deserve your approval or respect
85 ***absurd*** (page 60)
completely stupid, unreasonable, or impossible to believe
86 ***agitated*** (page 61)
worried or upset
87 ***ordeal*** (page 65)
an extremely unpleasant experience, especially one that lasts for a long time
88 ***infinitely*** (page 65)
very, or very much
89 ***exploded*** – *to explode something* (page 68)
to prove that a story or theory that many people believe is in fact false
90 ***whooping cough*** (page 69)
an infectious disease of children that causes them to cough and make a loud noise when they breathe

91 ***measles*** (page 69)
an infectious disease common in children in which there are red spots all over the body and a high temperature

92 ***Government Stocks*** (page 69)
a type of investment which is offered by the government and is considered to be safe and reliable

93 ***indignant*** (page 71)
angry because of an unfair situation or someone's unfair behaviour

94 ***celibate*** (page 73)
not married and never having sex, often because of religious beliefs

95 ***pram*** (page 74)
a large object with four wheels that a baby can lie in while you push it around. This is a shortened form of the original word *perambulator*, which is no longer used in English.

96 ***Army List*** (page 78)
an official list of all the officers in the British army which gives information about their position in the army and their careers

Useful Phrases

by the way (page 11)
used for introducing a new or extra fact or comment into a conversation

Good heavens (page 11)
used for showing that you are very surprised, angry or upset

I must say (page 15)
used in spoken English for emphasizing a statement

It's about time (page 20)
used for saying that someone should do something soon

runs in families – *something runs in the/someone's family* (page 29)
if something such as a quality or disease runs in someone's family, a lot of people in the family have it and it is passed from parents to their children in their genes

at a moment's notice (page 35)
without being given much warning before something happens

As a man sows, so shall he reap (page 40)
the most basic meaning of this phrase is that the seeds you plant in the ground – *sow* – will grow into the plants which you will cut and gather – *reap*. This phrase is used for saying that something happens to someone because of what they have done in the past. It was originally a religious phrase, but people use it now with a general meaning. Miss Prism says that Ernest died of a bad cold as a result of his bad behaviour.

bitter trials (page 41)
a *bitter trial* is a very painful or difficult experience

blessings in disguise (page 41)
Chasuble says that painful experiences – bitter trials – can be *blessings in disguise*. A *blessing* is something good that you feel very grateful or lucky to have. Chasuble is saying that something can seem to cause problems, but later you realize it is a good thing.

call a spade a spade (page 56)
to say very directly what you think about someone or something even if this is rude. A *spade* is a tool used for digging.

anybody who is anybody (page 56)
all people who are important or famous. Gwendolen is saying that she does not believe that any important people live in the countryside.

bores me to death – *to bore someone to death* (page 56)
to make someone feel extremely impatient or dissatisfied. The expression *to death* is used after a verb or an adjective to emphasize that someone feels something very strongly.

to say nothing of the fact that (page 61)
used for adding extra information to what you have just said

stand in my way – *to stand in someone's way* (page 70)
to stop or try to stop someone from doing something

comes of age – *to come of age* (page 70)
to reach the age when you are legally an adult

out of the question – *to be out of the question* (page 72)
used for saying that something is definitely not a possibility

in your own hands – *to be in someone's hands* (page 72)
if something is in someone's hands, they are responsible for it

Exercises

Background Information

Choose the correct information to complete the sentences.

1 Oscar Wilde was Irish / Scottish.

2 Wilde's father / mother was involved in working for independence for his / her country.

3 Wilde studied at Oxford / Cambridge University.

4 At university, Wilde got very good / bad grades.

5 As a student, Wilde won a prize for writing plays / poems.

6 Wilde was influenced by the writings of John Ruskin and Walter Pater on politics / beauty.

7 At the start of his career, Wilde wrote some short stories for his wife / children.

8 *The Picture of Dorian Gray* was the only play / novel which Wilde wrote.

9 Wilde was always / not always seen as a serious figure when he gave lectures.

10 Wilde's work included a play written in German / French.

11 Wilde was married / divorced at the time of his death.

12 Today, Wilde's serious / light-hearted works are best remembered.

13 In the twentieth century, one / several of Wilde's works led to (a) musical production(s).

14 *The Importance of Being Earnest* has been made into a film at least once / twice.

Multiple Choice

Tick the best answer.

1 What is Lady Bracknell's relationship to Algernon?

a She is his mother.

b She is his aunt. ✓

c She is his mother-in-law.

d There is no family relationship.

2 What reason does Jack give for coming to town in Act 1?

a To have tea with Algernon.

b To have dinner with Lady Bracknell.

c To propose to Gwendolen.

d To propose to Cecily.

3 How does Algernon discover that Jack's real name is not Ernest?

a By asking him about an inscription on a cigarette case.

b By asking his aunt, Lady Bracknell.

c By asking him about an inscription on a handbag.

d By going to his house in the country and asking Cecily.

4 Which of the following is NOT true about Jack and Algernon's imaginary characters?

a Algernon uses his imaginary friend as an excuse to avoid dinner with his aunt.

b Jack uses his imaginary brother as an excuse to come to town and have fun.

c Both of their imaginary characters are named Ernest.

d Algernon's imaginary friend is an invalid with poor health.

5 Why was Jack given the surname 'Worthing'?

a Because it was his father's name.

b Because he liked the town Worthing and decided to call himself this name.

c Because the man who found him had a ticket to Worthing in his pocket.

d Because there was a note in the handbag saying his name was Worthing.

6 Why does Jack return to his country home wearing black clothes?

a Because he is in mourning for his dead imaginary brother.

b Because it is fashionable to wear black in the country.

c Because he has been to a funeral.

d Because Thomas Cardew, the man who brought him up, has died.

7 Which of the following is NOT served as part of afternoon tea?

a Muffins.

b Tea.

c Coffee.

d Bread and butter.

8 Who tells Lady Bracknell the address that Gwendolen has gone to in the country?

a Algernon.

b Miss Prism.

c Lord Bracknell.

d A maid.

9 Why does Lady Bracknell consider Cecily a good future wife for Algernon?

a Because she is fashionable and attractive.

b Because she has a lot of money.

c Because she is a friend of Gwendolen's.

d Because she is in love with Algernon.

10 What is Jack's main reason for refusing to consent to Algernon marrying Cecily?

a He believes that Algernon does not love Cecily.

b He hopes to force Lady Bracknell to consent to his own marriage with Gwendolen.

c Algernon has no known parents.

d Algernon is not as rich as Cecily.

11 Why is Jack's real name Ernest at the end of the play?

a Because he asks Chasuble to baptize him with this name.

b Because Thomas Cardew baptized him as Ernest as a baby.

c Because Gwendolen insists that he is baptized with this name.

d Because his mother and father, also called Ernest, baptized him with this name.

Word Focus

Complete the table with the missing nouns. The missing nouns are all in the play.

NOUN	ADJECTIVE
1 *wickedness*	wicked
2	equal
3	hypocritical
4	careless
5	pleased
6	ignorant
7	romantic
8	amazed

Complete the sentences with one of the words from the table.

1 Algernon argues that whilst being in love is ....*romantic*............ , proposing marriage is not.

2 When Jack tells Lady Bracknell that he has lost both parents, she says that to lose one parent is unfortunate, but losing both suggests he is ....

3 Lady Bracknell is pleased to hear that Jack considers himself to know nothing, as for her, ... is better than education.

4 When accepting an offer, for example to go for a walk in the garden, a possible answer is, 'Yes, with .... '.

5 Cecily is a little frightened to meet Jack's .... brother, Ernest, as she has never met such a badly behaved person before.

6 Cecily tells Algernon, who she believes to be Ernest, that if he has been leading a double life and pretending to be bad while in fact being good, then this is a sign of ....

7 When Jack and Algernon agree to be baptized, Gwendolen sees this as a sign that there will never be .... between the sexes because men have a greater capacity for self-sacrifice than women.

8 Miss Prism is .... at the end of the play to discover that Jack is the baby she mistakenly left in the cloakroom in Victoria Station.

Vocabulary: Negative prefixes

Complete the gaps with a negative prefix *dis-*, *un-*, *mis-*, *in-* to form a word with the opposite meaning.

1 Lady Bracknell ...*dis*... approves of Jack marrying her daughter as he has no known relatives.

2 Algernon's imaginary friend is often ....well, which gives Algernon an excuse to visit him.

3 Jack thinks that his life story is perfectly ordinary and there is nothing ....believable about it.

4 Lady Bracknell thinks that Jack's house in London is on the ....fashionable side of the street.

5 Lady Bracknell states that an engagement should be a surprise to a girl, whether pleasant or ....pleasant, not something she plans herself.

6 Miss Prism believes that Jack's imaginary brother is weak and ....decisive, after hearing Jack's stories of Earnest's ....behaviour.

7 Merriman ....packs Algernon's luggage after his arrival at the house.

8 Gwendolen believes that Cecily's story about being engaged to Ernest is ....true.

9 Lady Bracknell forbids Algernon from being baptized, saying that it would ....please Lord Bracknell.

10 Miss Prism is happy to have her bag ....expectedly returned to her at the end of the play, saying that it was ....convenient to have lost it many years ago.

11 When Lady Bracknell is reminded of the general's name, Ernest, she remembers her reason for ....liking the name.

Vocabulary: Opposites

Tick the word which has the opposite meaning to the underlined word in each sentence.

1 Lady Bracknell <u>refuses</u> to consent to the marriage of Jack and Gwendolen.
- **a** rejects
- **b** agrees ✓
- **c** allows
- **d** enables

2 Gwendolen tells Jack that he is wonderfully <u>complicated</u>.
- **a** open
- **b** straight
- **c** bored
- **d** simple

3 Before discovering he has lied, Gwendolen claims that her 'Ernest' has a <u>truthful</u> nature.
- **a** lying
- **b** deceitful
- **c** unhelpful
- **d** honest

4 Miss Prism tells Chasuble that he can rely on a <u>mature</u> woman.
- **a** dishonest
- **b** young
- **c** poor
- **d** adult

5 Cecily believes that Jack's brother is a <u>wicked</u> man.
- **a** good
- **b** healthy
- **c** living
- **d** true

6 Believing her to be his mother, Jack says it could be a <u>serious</u> problem that Miss Prism is unmarried.
- **a** future
- **b** trivial
- **c** major
- **d** quite

Vocabulary: Formal language

Find a formal word or expression from the quotations for each explanation given below.

Algernon: My dear fellow, the way that you flirt with Gwendolen is perfectly disgraceful. (p 12)

Jack: You ought to dine with your Aunt Augusta. (p 18)

Algernon: Good heavens! Lane! Why are there no cucumber sandwiches? (p 20)

Jack: I beg your pardon, Algy, I suppose I shouldn't talk about your own aunt in that way. (p 27)

Chasuble: It would be a pleasure, Miss Prism, a pleasure. Let us go to the end of the garden and back. (p 36)

Jack: You young scoundrel, Algy, you must get out of this place as soon as possible. (p 44)

Cecily: When one is dictating, one should speak clearly and not cough. (p 47)

Gwendolen: Outside the family circle, Papa, I am glad to say, is completely unknown. (p 52)

1 father ....*Papa*........
2 expression showing surprise or anger ....
3 pronoun used to mean 'you' or people in general ....
4 expression used to address a male friend ....
5 expression used to make a suggestion, now abbreviated to Let's ....
6 name for a man who behaves badly or dishonestly ....
7 expression to accept an invitation ....
8 expression meaning 'I'm sorry'/'Excuse me' ....
9 verb meaning 'have dinner' ....
10 adverb and adjective meaning socially unacceptable ....

Useful Phrases

Complete the sentences. Use each phrase from the box once.

bitter trial	blessing in disguise	bores her to death
call a spade a spade	come of age	in her own hands
out of the question	~~runs in families~~	

1 When debating how to kill off his imaginary brother, Algernon warns Jack not to choose a hereditary condition which ....*runs in families*........ such as heart attacks.

2 After the death of Jack's imaginary brother, Chasuble tells Jack not to grieve too much, suggesting that the death of this wicked man might be a ....

3 Chasuble refers to the painful experience of Ernest's death as a ....

4 Cecily angrily tells Gwendolen that it is important to be direct and honest and .... , rather than pretending to have good manners when in fact you are rude.

5 Gwendolen tells Cecily that she cannot imagine how anyone lives in the country, a place which ....

6 Jack informs Lady Bracknell that Cecily will only .... when she is thirty-five according to her grandfather's will.

7 Cecily says that she hates waiting and therefore waiting until she is thirty-five to get married is completely ....

8 Jack informs Lady Bracknell that the decision about Algernon and Cecily's future is ....

Grammar: Question tags

Complete the questions from the play with a question tag from the box. There are three which you do not need.

aren't you	does it	don't you	may I not	~~is it not~~
can't I	won't you	doesn't it	may you	

1 Then that is all quite settled, ...*is it not*...... ?

2 I can dine with you tonight, ... ?

3 You will marry me, ... ?

4 Hopelessly doesn't make much sense, ... ?

5 I may call you Cecily, ... ?

6 You often baptize people, ... ?

Which two of the question tags above are old-fashioned and formal?

1 ......*may I not?*......

2 ....

How could they be said in a less formal, more modern way?

1 ......*I can call you Cecily, can't I?*......

2 ....

Now add modern question tags to the following questions.

1 You're not married, ...*are you*...... ?

2 She lives in the country, ... ?

3 He won't marry her daughter, ... ?

4 It's difficult to lead a double life, ... ?

5 You can't get married before you come of age, ... ?

6 His brother behaved in a wicked way, ... ?

Grammar: Relative clauses

Rewrite the two sentences to make one sentence using a relative pronoun, *which, that, who, where* or *whose*.

1 Miss Prism left a bag at Victoria Station. The bag contained a baby.
Miss Prism ......*left a bag which contained a baby at Victoria Station*...... .

2 Thomas Cardew made Jack the guardian of Cecily. Thomas Cardew found Jack as a baby.
Thomas Cardew ....
....

3 Lady Bracknell does not want her daughter to marry Jack. Jack has no known relations.
Lady Bracknell ....
....

4 Algernon writes down the address of Jack's country home. Cecily lives in Jack's country home.
Algernon ....
....

5 Cecily is frightened of meeting Ernest. Ernest's behaviour is wicked.
Cecily ....
....

6 Cecily keeps a diary. She writes her secrets in it.
Cecily ....
....

7 Jack refuses to consent to Cecily's marriage. This means she cannot marry until she is thirty-five.
Jack ....
....

8 Jack's father baptized his son with the same name. Jack's father's name was Ernest.
Jack's father ....
....

Published by Macmillan Heinemann ELT
Between Towns Road, Oxford OX4 3PP
A division of Macmillan Publishers Limited
Companies and representatives throughout the world
Heinemann is the registered trademark of Pearson Education, used under licence.

ISBN 978–0–2304–0844–9
ISBN 978–0–2304–0868–5 (with CD edition)

This version of *The Importance of Being Earnest* was retold by F H Cornish for Macmillan Readers.

First published 2011

Illustrated by Gavin Reece
Cover photograph by Corbis / Condé Nast Archive

Printed and bound in Thailand

without CD edition
2016 2015 2014 2013 2012 2011
10 9 8 7 6 5 4 3 2

with CD pack edition
2016 2015 2014 2013 2012 2011
10 9 8 7 6 5 4 3 2 1